Sign Up Online

HIGH SCHOOL ELA-2 Practice

Get Digital Access To

2 ELA-2 Practice Tests

5 ELA-2 Domains

Register Now

Url: www.lumoslearning.com/a/tedbooks

Access Code: **ELA2HS-83149-P**

High School ELA 2 Practice Workbook - English Language Arts Online Assessments and Standards-based Lessons: Lumos Skills Mastery Grade 10

Contributing Author - **Frances Havard**
Contributing Author - **Stephanie Green**
Contributing Author - **Tom Farr**
Contributing Author - **Dana Ahmuty**
Contributing Author - **Amy Flanders**
Executive Producer - **Mukunda Krishnaswamy**
Designer and Illustrator - **Tanuja Prakash**

ISBN-10: 1949855171

ISBN-13: 978-1949855173

Printed in the United States of America

For permissions and additional information contact us

Lumos Information Services, LLC
PO Box 1575, Piscataway, NJ 08855-1575
http://www.LumosLearning.com

Email: support@lumoslearning.com
Tel: (732) 384-0146
Fax: (866) 283-6471

Table of Contents

INTRODUCTION

This book is designed to help students get High School ELA 2 rehearsal along with standards aligned with rigorous skills practice. ELA 2 is one of the credits that students will have to earn as a part of English Language Arts credit requirement for High School Graduation.

Unlike a traditional book, this Lumos tedBook offers two full-length practice tests in the online version. Taking these tests will not only help students get a comprehensive review of standards assessed in ELA 2 but also become familiar with technology-enhanced question types.

After students take the test online, educators can use the score report to assign specific lessons provided in this book.

Students will obtain a better understanding of each standard and improve on their weaknesses by practicing the content of this workbook. The lessons contain rigorous questions aligned to the state standards and substandards. Taking the time to work through the activities will enable students to become proficient in each grade level standard.

About Lumos Smart Test Prep Methodology:

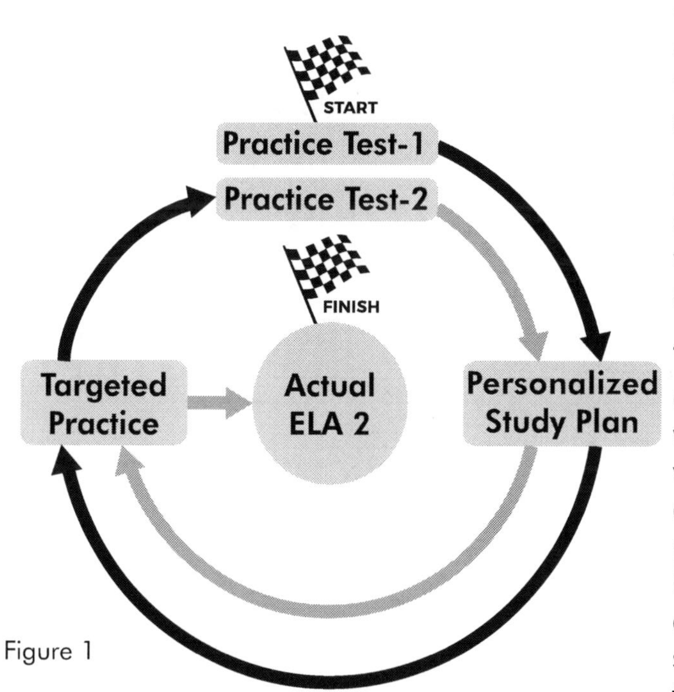

Figure 1

With more than a decade of experience and expertise in developing practice resources for standardized tests, Lumos Learning has developed the most efficient methodology to help students succeed on the state assessments (See Figure 1).

Lumos Smart Test Prep Methodology offers students realistic ELA 2 assessment rehearsal along with providing an efficient pathway to overcome each proficiency gap.

The process starts with students taking the online diagnostic assessment. This online diagnostic test will help assess students' proficiency levels in various standards. With the completion of this diagnostic assessment, Lumos generates a personalized study plan with a standard checklist based on student performance in the online diagnostic test. Parents and educators can use this study plan to remediate the proficiency gaps with targeted standards-based practice available in the workbook.

After student completes the targeted remedial practice, they should attempt the second online ELA 2 practice test. Upon finishing the second assessment, Lumos will generate another individualized study plan by identifying topics that require more practice. Based on these practice suggestions, further skill-building activities can be planned to help students gain comprehensive mastery needed to ensure success on the state assessment.

How will Lumos StepUp® program help students in preparing for the end of course exams of High School ELA credit programs?

The Lumos StepUp® program for High School ELA courses includes

(a) Two Full-length practice tests

(b) Get realistic practice through Online Assessments. It gives students the opportunity to practice test-taking skills, familiarize with the format of the test, and efficiently review the key topics. The results will help you get insights into your child's strengths and weaknesses in various content areas. These insights could be used to help your child strengthen their skills in topics where they are having difficulty. This test practice helps them improve speed and accuracy while taking the actual High School ELA 2 Assessments.

(c) StepUp® has great learning content with access to hundreds of activities and Online workbooks.

(d) Your child's work is carefully and meticulously tracked throughout the program. Easy-to-use, advanced and real-time reports will help you identify weak areas and tailor personalized learning plans for your child.

(e) The StepUp® program allows your child to prepare at a pace that is right for him or her. This student-centric approach, combined with instant feedback boosts student confidence and improves learning outcomes.

(f) StepUp® program can be accessed through a number of devices that include, PC, tablet and smartphones and it is available 24×7. This convenience helps to enable anywhere learning.

Chapter 1

Lumos Smart Test Prep Methodology

Step 1: Access Online ELA2 Practice Test

The online ELA2 practice tests mirror the actual English Language Arts in the number of questions, item types, test duration, test tools, and more.

After completing the test, your student will receive immediate feedback with detailed reports on standards mastery and a personalized study plan to overcome any learning gaps. With this study plan, use the next section of the workbook to practice.

Use the URL and access code provided below or scan the QR code to access the first ELA2 practice test to get started.

URL	QR Code
Visit the URL below and place the book access code **www.lumoslearning.com/a/tedbooks** **Access Code: ELA2HS-83149-P**	

Step 2: Review the Personalized Study Plan Online

After students complete the online Practice Test 1, they can access their individualized study plan from the table of contents (Figure 2) Parents and Teachers can also review the study plan through their Lumos account (parent or teacher) portal.

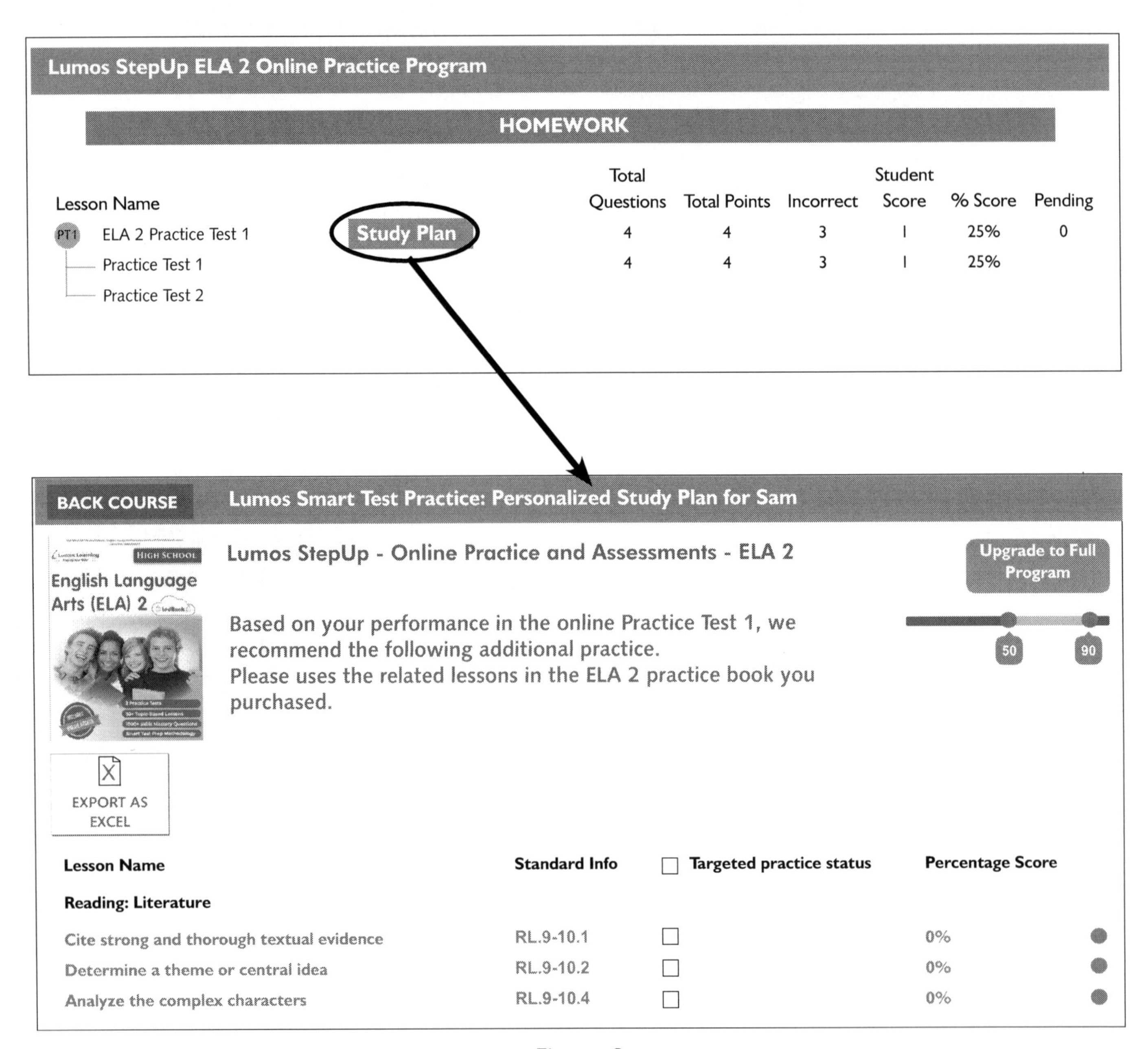

Figure 2

Step 3: Complete Targeted Practice

Using the information provided in the study plan report, complete the targeted practice using the appropriate lessons to overcome proficiency gaps. With lesson names included in the study plan, find the appropriate topics in this workbook and answer the questions provided. Students can refer to the answer key and detailed answers provided for each lesson to gain further understanding of the learning objective. Marking the completed lessons in the study plan after each practice session is recommended.(See Figure 3)

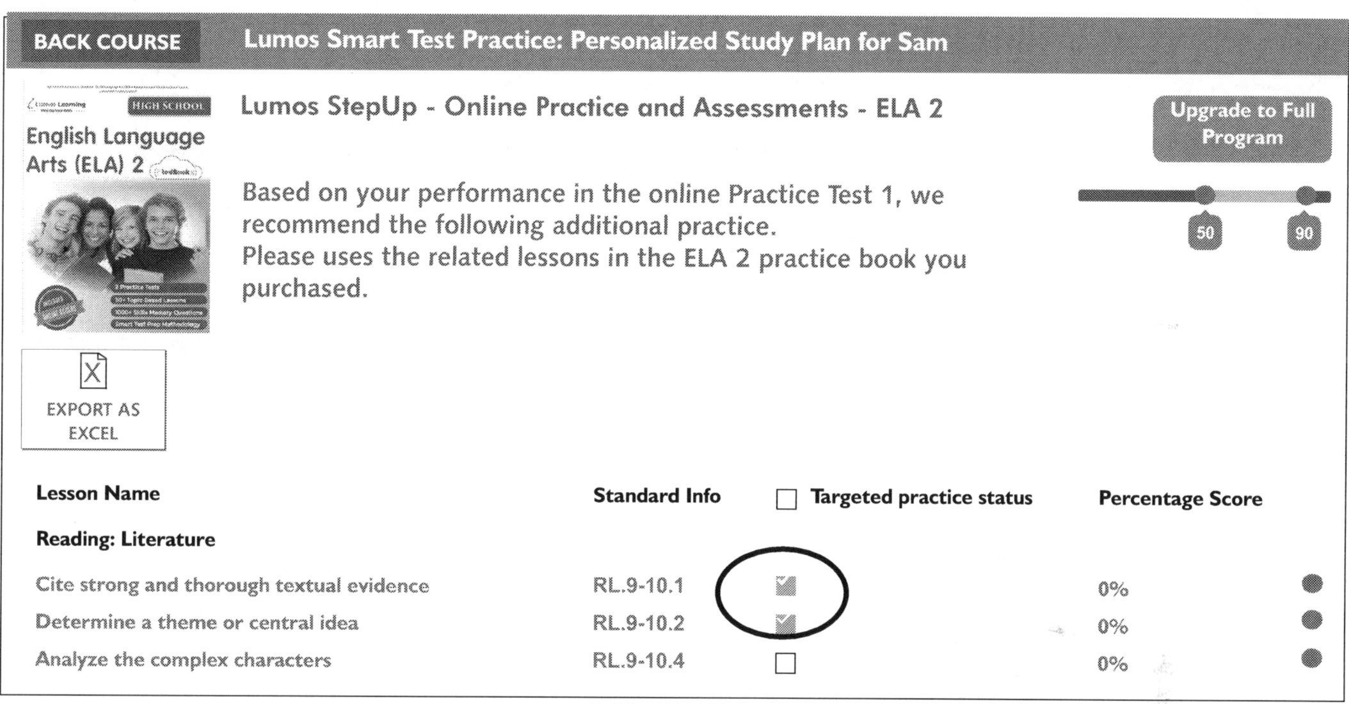

Figure 3

Step 4: Access the Practice Test 2 Online

After completing the targeted practice in this workbook, students should attempt the second ELA 2 practice test online. Using the student login name and password, login to the Lumos website to complete the second practice test.

Step 5: Repeat Targeted Practice

Repeat the targeted practice as per Step 3 using the second study plan report for Practice test 2 after completion of the second ELA 2 rehearsal.

Visit www.lumoslearning.com/a/lstp for more information on Lumos Smart Testprep Methodology or Scan the QR Code	

What if I buy more than one Lumos Study Program?

Step 1 ⟶ **Visit the URL given below and login to your account**

www.lumoslearning.com

Step 2 ⟶ Click on **'My Subscriptions'** under the **"Account"** tab and goto **"My tedBook"**

Place the Book Access Code and submit.

Step 3 ⟶ **Add the new book**

To add the new book for a registered student, choose the '**Existing Student**' button, select the student and submit.

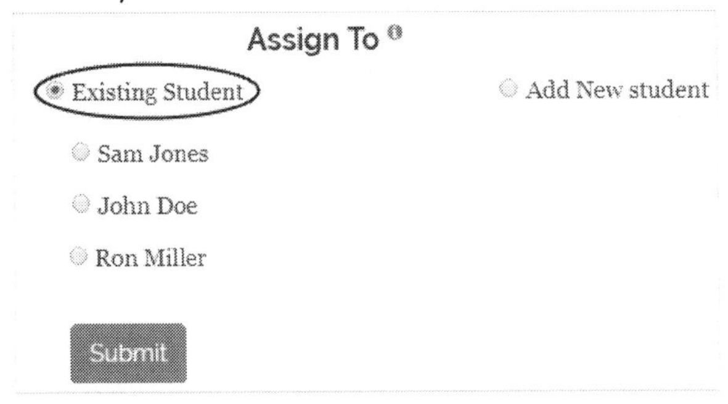

To add the new book for a new student, choose the '**Add New Student**' button and complete the student registration.

Assign To

Existing Student

Add New student

Register Your TedBook

Student Name:* Enter First Name Enter Last Name

Student Login*

Password*

Submit

Test Taking Tips

1) **The day before the test,** make sure you get a good night's sleep.

2) **On the day of the test,** be sure to eat a good hearty breakfast! Also, be sure to arrive at school on time.

3) **During the test:**

- **Read every question carefully.**
  - Do not spend too much time on any one question. Work steadily through all questions in the section.
  - Attempt all of the questions even if you are not sure of some answers.
  - If you run into a difficult question, eliminate as many choices as you can and then pick the best one from the remaining choices. Intelligent guessing will help you increase your score.
  - Also, mark the question so that if you have extra time, you can return to it after you reach the end of the section.
  - Some questions may refer to a graph, chart, or other kind of picture. Carefully review the graphic before answering the question.
  - Be sure to include explanations for your written responses and show all work.

- **While Answering TECR questions.**
  - Read the directions of each question. Some might ask you to drag something, others to select, and still, others to highlight. Follow all instructions of the question (or questions if it is in multiple parts)

Name: ______________________ Date: ______________

Reading: Literature

Passage 1: Down The Rabbit Hole

(1) Alice was beginning to get very tired of sitting by her sister on the bank, and of having nothing to do: once or twice she had peeped into the book her sister was reading, but it had no pictures or conversations in it, 'and what is the use of a book,' thought Alice 'without pictures or conversations?'

(2) So she was considering in her own mind (as well as she could, for the hot day made her feel very sleepy and stupid), whether the pleasure of making a daisy-chain would be worth the trouble of getting up and picking the daisies, when suddenly a White Rabbit with pink eyes ran close by her.

(3) There was nothing so very remarkable in that; nor did Alice think it so very much out of the way to hear the Rabbit say to itself, 'Oh dear! Oh dear! I shall be late!' (when she thought it over afterwards, it occurred to her that she ought to have wondered at this, but at the time it all seemed quite natural); but when the Rabbit actually took a watch out of its waistcoat-pocket, and looked at it, and then hurried on, Alice started to her feet, for it flashed across her mind that she had never before seen a rabbit with either a waistcoat-pocket, or a watch to take out of it, and burning with curiosity, she ran across the field after it, and fortunately was just in time to see it pop down a large rabbit-hole under the hedge.

(4) In another moment down went Alice after it, never once considering how in the world she was to get out again.

(5) The rabbit-hole went straight on like a tunnel for some way, and then dipped suddenly down, so suddenly that Alice had not a moment to think about stopping herself before she found herself falling down a very deep well.

(6) Either the well was very deep, or she fell very slowly, for she had plenty of time as she went down to look about her and to wonder what was going to happen next. First, she tried to look down and make out what she was coming to, but it was too dark to see anything; then she looked at the sides of the well, and noticed that they were filled with cupboards and book-shelves; here and there she saw maps and pictures hung upon pegs. She took down a jar from one of the shelves as she passed; it was labelled 'ORANGE MARMALADE', but to her great disappointment it was empty: she did not like to drop the jar for fear of killing somebody, so managed to put it into one of the cupboards as she fell past it.

(7) 'Well!' thought Alice to herself, 'after such a fall as this, I shall think nothing of tumbling down stairs! How brave they'll all think me at home! Why, I wouldn't say anything about it, even if I fell off the top of the house!' (Which was very likely true.)

(8) Down, down, down. Would the fall never come to an end! 'I wonder how many miles I've fallen by this time?' she said aloud. 'I must be getting somewhere near the centre of the earth. Let me see: that would be four thousand miles down, I think—' (for, you see, Alice had learnt several things of this sort in her lessons in the schoolroom, and though this was not a very good opportunity for showing off her knowledge, as there was no one to listen to her, still it was good practice to say it over) '—yes, that's about the right distance—but then I wonder what Latitude or Longitude I've got to?' (Alice had no idea what Latitude was, or Longitude either, but thought they were nice grand words to say.)

(9) Presently she began again. 'I wonder if I shall fall right through the earth! How funny it'll seem to come out among the people that walk with their heads downward! The Antipathies, I think—' (she was rather glad there was no one listening, this time, as it didn't sound at all the right word) '—but I shall have to ask them what the name of the country is, you know. Please, Ma'am, is this New Zealand or Australia?' (and she tried to curtsey as she spoke—fancy curtseying as you're falling through the air! Do you think you could manage it?) 'And what an ignorant little girl she'll think me for asking! No, it'll never do to ask: perhaps I shall see it written up somewhere.'

(10) Down, down, down. There was nothing else to do, so Alice soon began talking again. 'Dinah'll miss me very much to-night, I should think!' (Dinah was the cat.) 'I hope they'll remember her saucer of milk at tea-time. Dinah my dear! I wish you were down here with me! There are no mice in the air, I'm afraid, but you might catch a bat, and that's very like a mouse, you know. But do cats eat bats, I wonder?' And here Alice began to get rather sleepy, and went on saying to herself, in a dreamy sort of way, 'Do cats eat bats? Do cats eat bats?' and sometimes, 'Do bats eat cats?' for, you see, as she couldn't answer either question, it didn't much matter which way she put it. She felt that she was dozing off, and had just begun to dream that she was walking hand in hand with Dinah, and saying to her very earnestly, 'Now, Dinah, tell me the truth: did you ever eat a bat?' when suddenly, thump! thump! down she came upon a heap of sticks and dry leaves, and the fall was over.

(11) Alice was not a bit hurt, and she jumped up on to her feet in a moment: she looked up, but it was all dark overhead; before her was another long passage, and the White Rabbit was still in sight, hurrying down it. There was not a moment to be lost: away went Alice like the wind, and was just in time to hear it say, as it turned a corner, 'Oh my ears and whiskers, how late it's getting!' She was close behind it when she turned the corner, but the Rabbit was no longer to be seen: she found herself in a long, low hall, which was lit up by a row of lamps hanging from the roof.

(12) There were doors all round the hall, but they were all locked; and when Alice had been all the way down one side and up the other, trying every door, she walked sadly down the middle, wondering how she was ever to get out again.

(13) Suddenly she came upon a little three-legged table, all made of solid glass; there was nothing on it except a tiny golden key, and Alice's first thought was that it might belong to one of the doors of the hall; but, alas! either the locks were too large, or the key was too small, but at any rate, it would not open any of them. However, on the second time around, she came upon a low curtain she had not noticed before, and behind it was a little door about fifteen inches high: she tried the little golden key in the lock, and to her great delight it fitted!

(14) Alice opened the door and found that it led into a small passage, not much larger than a rat-hole: she knelt down and looked along the passage into the loveliest garden you ever saw. How she longed to get out of that dark hall, and wander about among those beds of bright flowers and those cool fountains, but she could not even get her head through the doorway; 'and even if my head would go through,' thought poor Alice, 'it would be of very little use without my shoulders. Oh, how I wish I could shut up like a telescope! I think I could, if I only knew how to begin.' For, you see, so many out-of-the-way things had happened lately, that Alice had begun to think that very few things indeed were really impossible.

(15) There seemed to be no use in waiting by the little door, so she went back to the table, half hoping she might find another key on it, or at any rate a book of rules for shutting people up like telescopes: this time she found a little bottle on it, ('which certainly was not here before,' said Alice,) and round the neck of the bottle was a paper label, with the words 'DRINK ME' beautifully printed on it in large letters.

(16) It was all very well to say 'Drink me,' but the wise little Alice was not going to do that in a hurry. 'No, I'll look first,' she said, 'and see whether it's marked "poison" or not'; for she had read several nice little histories about children who had got burnt, and eaten up by wild beasts and other unpleasant things, all because they would not remember the simple rules their friends had taught them: such as, that a red-hot poker will burn you if you hold it too long; and that if you cut your finger very deeply with a knife, it usually bleeds; and she had never forgotten that, if you drink much from a bottle marked 'poison,' it is almost certain to disagree with you, sooner or later.

(17) However, this bottle was not marked 'poison,' so Alice ventured to taste it, and finding it very nice, (it had, in fact, a sort of mixed flavour of cherry-tart, custard, pine-apple, roast turkey, toffee, and hot buttered toast,) she very soon finished it off.

1. Alice's character is established in the opening paragraph. What can we infer about Alice's character based on the comment: "and what is the use of a book,' thought Alice 'without pictures or conversations?'

Ⓐ She is a boring person.
Ⓑ She doesn't like her sister.
Ⓒ She is silly.
Ⓓ She is curious about people and their conversations.

2. Which character trait is BEST established in the following excerpt? "In another moment down went Alice after it, never once considering how in the world she was to get out again."

Ⓐ Silly
Ⓑ Brave
Ⓒ Impulsive
Ⓓ Angry

3. In paragraphs 5-7, what tone is established by the writer as Alice moves through the tunnel?

Ⓐ Scared
Ⓑ Curious
Ⓒ Awestruck
Ⓓ Assertive

4. In paragraph 9, Caroll writes, "The Antipathies, I think--' (she was rather glad there was no one listening, this time, as it didn't sound at all the right word)." Why do you think she chooses to reveal this lack of knowledge about Alice? How does it add to her character?

Ⓐ It makes Alice seem silly, so the reader feels sorry for her.
Ⓑ It makes Alice seem more human so that the reader connects with her.
Ⓒ It encourages the reader to learn a new word.
Ⓓ It encourages the reader to think of the book.

5.When Alice lands at the bottom, she tries to get outside. She realizes she can't and says "Oh, how I wish I could shut up like a telescope!" which literary device does the author use in this sentence?

Ⓐ Personification
Ⓑ Simile
Ⓒ Metaphor
Ⓓ Theme

6.When Alice says "Oh, how I wish I could shut up like a telescope!", the writer wants you to compare Alice to a telescope because

Ⓐ Telescopes can see things from far away.
Ⓑ Telescopes can be very useful tools.
Ⓒ Telescopes have a lens that shrinks to see things from far away.
Ⓓ None of the above.

7. Which sentence best indicates a playful tone; a tone in which Carroll attempts to capture the childlike wonder of Alice's character?

Ⓐ However, this bottle was not marked 'poison,' so Alice ventured to taste it, and finding it very nice, (it had, in fact, a sort of mixed flavour of cherry-tart, custard, pine-apple, roast turkey, toffee, and hot buttered toast,) she very soon finished it off.
Ⓑ Either the well was very deep, or she fell very slowly, for she had plenty of time as she went down to look about her and to wonder what was going to happen next.
Ⓒ (Alice had no idea what Latitude was, or Longitude either, but thought they were nice grand words to say.)
Ⓓ All of the above.

8. Choose a paragraph from the list below, where the author spends a lot of time describing the setting. Write the correct answer in the box below.

Ⓐ Paragraph 1
Ⓑ Paragraph 6
Ⓒ Paragraph 10
Ⓓ Paragraph 17

9.The narrator of the passage can best be described as

Ⓐ First Person
Ⓑ Second Person
Ⓒ Third Person Omniscient
Ⓓ Third Person Limited

10. The narrator can easily see inside Alice's head which makes the tale a 3rd person narrative (using he or she), but because we cannot see inside the rabbit's or the sister's head, the view is also considered limited.
As the passage develops, Alice's character goes from being

Ⓐ Curious to determined
Ⓑ Silly to weepy
Ⓒ Brave to scared
Ⓓ Indifferent to bored

Passage 2: A Psalm of Life

1. Tell me not, in mournful numbers,
Life is but an empty dream!
For the soul is dead that slumbers,
And things are not what they seem.

2. Life is real! Life is earnest!
And the grave is not its goal;
Dust thou art, to dust returnest,
Was not spoken of the soul.

3. Not enjoyment, and not sorrow,
Is our destined end or way;
But to act, that each to-morrow
Find us farther than to-day.

4. Art is long, and Time is fleeting,
And our hearts, though stout and brave,
Still, like muffled drums, are beating
Funeral marches to the grave.

5. In the world's broad field of battle,
In the bivouac of Life,
Be not like dumb, driven cattle!
Be a hero in the strife!

6. Trust no Future, howe'er pleasant!
Let the dead Past bury its dead!
Act,— act in the living Present!
Heart within, and God o'erhead!

7. Lives of great men all remind us
We can make our lives sublime,
And, departing, leave behind us
Footprints on the sands of time;

8. Footprints, that perhaps another,
Sailing o'er life's solemn main,
A forlorn and shipwrecked brother,
Seeing, shall take heart again.

9. Let us, then, be up and doing,
With a heart for any fate;
Still achieving, still pursuing,
Learn to labor and to wait.

1.The narrator of the poem or the persona of the poem can best be described as

Ⓐ Bored
Ⓑ Commanding
Ⓒ Tired
Ⓓ Thoughtful

2.In the first sentence, who is the narrator speaking to when he remarks "Tell me not, in mournful numbers, Life is but an empty dream!"?

Ⓐ Psalmist
Ⓑ His friend
Ⓒ His uncle
Ⓓ No one

3. In stanza one, the line "For the soul is dead that slumbers" refers to

Ⓐ People who lie in their beds for too long.
Ⓑ People who do too much with their spare time.
Ⓒ People who do too little and are in a "sleep-like state."
Ⓓ People who live life to the fullest.

4. True or False. In stanza 3, the line "But to act, that each to-morrow/ Find us farther than to-day" best reflects the theme or action and growth as being defining concepts to live one's life.

Ⓐ True
Ⓑ False

Name: ______________________ Date: ______________

5.Determine whether the following statement is True or False.

	True	False
This line in stanza 9 uses a metaphor: Let us, then, be up and doing		

6. Who does the narrator reference in stanza 7 that should be an inspiration to us?

Ⓐ great men
Ⓑ shipwrecked brother
Ⓒ the soul
Ⓓ the readers

7. Theme can best be described as

Ⓐ The story's main message
Ⓑ The conflict
Ⓒ The plot events
Ⓓ The characters

8. Why is it important that the reader be aware of the climax of a piece of writing when trying to understand the theme?

9. Arrange the following list in the order of how you should understand the theme

Ⓐ identify the climax of the story
Ⓑ identify the important elements of the plot
Ⓒ analyze how the main character grows in the denouement
Ⓓ connect the growth of the character to lessons in the real

10.Determine whether the following statement is True or False.

Imagery is a tool used by a writer to help shape the theme.	

Passage 3: Our story today is called "The Birthmark"

A long time ago, there lived a skillful scientist who had experienced a spiritual reaction more striking than any chemical one. He had left his laboratory in the care of his assistant, washed the chemicals from his hands, and asked a beautiful woman to become his wife. In those days new scientific discoveries such as electricity seemed to open paths into the area of miracles. It was not unusual for the love of science to compete with the love of a woman.

The scientist's name was Aylmer. He had so totally given himself to scientific studies that he could not be weakened by a second love. His love for his young wife could only be the stronger of the two if it could link itself with his love of science. Such a union did take place with truly remarkable results. But one day, very soon after their marriage, Aylmer looked at his wife with a troubled expression.

"Georgiana," he said, "have you ever considered that the mark upon your cheek might be removed"?

"No," she said smiling. But seeing the seriousness of his question, she said, "The mark has so often been called a charm that I was simple enough to imagine it might be so."

"On another face it might," answered her husband, "but not on yours. No dear, Nature made you so perfectly that this small defect shocks me as being a sign of earthly imperfection."

"Shocks you!" cried Georgiana, deeply hurt. Her face reddened and she burst into tears. "Then why did you marry me? You cannot love what shocks you!"

We must explain that in the center of Georgiana's left cheek there was a mark, deep in her skin. The mark was usually a deep red color. When Georgiana blushed, the mark became less visible. But when she turned pale, there was the mark, like a red stain upon snow.

The birthmark would come and go with the emotions in her heart. The mark was shaped like a very small human hand. Georgiana's past lovers used to say that the hand of a magical fairy had touched her face when she was born. Many a gentleman would have risked his life for the honor of kissing that mysterious hand. But other people had different opinions. Some women said the red hand quite destroyed the effect of Georgiana's beauty. Male observers who did not praise the mark simply wished it away so that they did not see it. After his marriage, Aylmer discovered that this was the case with himself.

Had Georgiana been less beautiful, he might have felt his love increased by the prettiness of that little hand. But because she was otherwise so perfect, he found the mark had become unbearable.

Name: ______________________ Date: ______________

Aylmer saw the mark as a sign of his wife's eventual sadness, sickness, and death. Soon, the birthmark caused him more pain than Georgiana's beauty had ever given him pleasure.

During a period that should have been their happiest, Aylmer could only think of this disastrous subject. With the morning light, Aylmer opened his eyes upon his wife's face and recognized the sign of imperfection. When they sat together in the evening near the fire, he would look at the mark.

Georgiana soon began to fear his look. His expression would make her face go pale. And the birthmark would stand out like a red jewel on white stone.

"Do you remember, dear Aylmer, about the dream you had last night about this hateful mark?" she asked with a weak smile.

"None! None whatever!" answered Aylmer, surprised.

The mind is in a sad state when sleep cannot control its ghosts and allows them to break free with their secrets. Aylmer now remembered his dream. He had imagined himself with his assistant Aminadab trying to remove the birthmark with an operation. But the deeper his knife went, the deeper the small hand sank until it had caught hold of Georgiana's heart.

Aylmer felt guilty remembering the dream.

"Aylmer," said Georgiana, "I do not know what the cost would be to both of us to remove this birthmark. Removing it could deform my face or damage my health." "Dearest Georgiana, I have spent much thought on the subject," said Aylmer. "I am sure it can be removed." "Then let the attempt be made at any risk," said Georgiana. "Life is not worth living while this hateful mark makes me the object of your horror. You have deep science and have made great discoveries. Remove this little mark for the sake of your peace and my own." "Dearest wife," cried Aylmer. "Do not doubt my power. I am ready to make this cheek as perfect as its pair."

Her husband gently kissed her right cheek, the one without the red hand.

The next day the couple went to Aylmer's laboratory where he had made all his famous discoveries. Georgiana would live in a beautiful room he had prepared nearby, while he worked tirelessly in his lab. One by one, Aylmer tried a series of powerful experiments on his wife. But the mark remained.

Georgiana waited in her room. She read through his notebooks of scientific observations. She could not help see that many of his experiments had ended in failure. She decided to see for herself the scientist at work.

The first thing that struck Georgiana when entering the laboratory was the hot furnace. From the amount of soot above it, it seemed to have been burning for ages.

She saw machines, tubes, cylinders, and other containers for chemical experiments. What most drew her attention was Aylmer himself. He was nervous and pale as death as he worked on preparing a liquid. Georgiana realized that her husband had been hiding his tension and fear. "Think not so little of me that you cannot be honest about the risks we are taking," she said. "I will drink whatever you make for me, even if it is a poison." "My dear, nothing shall be hidden," Aylmer said. "I have already given you chemicals powerful enough to change your entire physical system. Only one thing remains to be tried and if that fails, we are ruined!"

He led her back to her room where she waited once more, alone with her thoughts. She hoped that for just one moment she could satisfy her husband's highest ideals. But she realized then that his mind would forever be on the march, always requiring something newer, better, and more perfect.

Hours later, Aylmer returned carrying a crystal glass with a colorless liquid. "The chemical process went perfectly," he said. "Unless all my science has tricked me, it cannot fail."

To test the liquid, he placed a drop in the soil of a dying flower growing in a pot in the room. In a few moments, the plant became healthy and green once more. "I do not need proof," Georgiana said quietly. "Give me the glass. I am happy to put my life in your hands." She drank the liquid and immediately fell asleep.

Aylmer sat next to his wife, observing her and taking notes. He noted everything -- her breathing, the movement of an eyelid. He stared at the birthmark. And slowly, with every breath that came and went, it lost some of its brightness.

"By Heaven! It is nearly gone," said Aylmer. "Success! Success!"

He opened the window coverings to see her face in daylight. She was so pale. Georgiana opened her eyes and looked into the mirror her husband held. She tried to smile as she saw the barely visible mark.

"My poor Aylmer," she said gently. "You have aimed so high. With so high and pure a feeling, you have rejected the best the Earth could offer. I am dying, dearest."

It was true. The hand on her face had been her link to life. As the last trace of color disappeared from her cheek, she gave her last breath.

Blinded by a meaningless imperfection and an impossible goal, Aylmer had thrown away her life and with it his chance for happiness. In trying to improve his lovely wife, he had failed to realize she had been perfect all along.

"The Birthmark" was written by Nathaniel Hawthorne. It was adapted and produced by Dana Demange.

Name: ______________________ Date: ______________

1.What type of character can Alymer best be described as?

Ⓐ Protagonist and Flat
Ⓑ Protagonist and Dynamic
Ⓒ Antagonist and Flat
Ⓓ Antagonist and Round

2.Which characteristic BEST describes Alymer's dominant trait?

Ⓐ Funny
Ⓑ Depressed
Ⓒ Lonely
Ⓓ Obsessive

3.Which character trait of his makes him kill his wife?

Ⓐ Funny
Ⓑ Depressed
Ⓒ Lonely
Ⓓ Obsessive

4. How does Alymer change over the course of the text?

Ⓐ He is completely obsessed with science and remains that way throughout the text.
Ⓑ He is depressed in the beginning and searching for a wife, but by the end he is glad to be a scientist again.
Ⓒ He can only focus on one thing at a time in the beginning, which is why he chooses a wife, but by the end he is relieved to be a scientist so he can fix her.
Ⓓ He can only focus on one thing at a time in the beginning, which is why he chooses a wife over his study of science, but by the end he is saddened because science ultimately destroys his wife.

5.The closing line of this abridged copy of the story is: "In trying to improve his lovely wife, he had failed to realize she had been perfect all along." Which story element is BEST emphasized in this line?

Ⓐ Theme
Ⓑ Conflict
Ⓒ Character development
Ⓓ All of the above

Name: ______________________ Date: ____________

6.How does Alymer's reaction to the birthmark differ from the other men who have known Georgina?

Ⓐ The other men who knew Georgina found it 'magical'.
Ⓑ The other men are disgusted by it too.
Ⓒ Alymer finds it beautiful and mysterious, but the other men don't.
Ⓓ The other men think it is a sign that no one should marry Georgina.

7.Which quotes from the text emphasizes Alymer's obsessive nature?

Ⓐ "He had so totally given himself to scientific studies that he could not be weakened by a second love"
Ⓑ "Life is not worth living while this hateful mark makes me the object of your horror." (Georgiania says to Alymer)"
Ⓒ "His love for his young wife could only be the stronger of the two if it could link itself with his love of science."
Ⓓ All of the above

8. How does the flaw in Alymer's character emphasize the theme? Write the correct answer in the box below.

Ⓐ It shows that we should keep working at things until we are satisfied.
Ⓑ It emphasizes that striving for perfection, can hurt those around us.
Ⓒ It emphasizes that science always triumphs over nature.
Ⓓ It emphasizes that marriage and love are more valuable than science.

9. Indirect characterization is used

Ⓐ When we learn about a character through what another character says about them.
Ⓑ When something is directly stated about a character by the narrator.
Ⓒ When we uncover something about a character by analyzing how they dress or speak.
Ⓓ All of the above.

10. Identify one quote from the story that shows Alymer being indirectly characterized by Georgiana's thoughts.

Passage 4: Hope is the thing with feathers

"Hope" is the thing with feathers -
That perches in the soul -
And sings the tune without the words -
And never stops - at all -

And sweetest - in the Gale - is heard -
And sore must be the storm -
That could abash the little Bird
That kept so many warm -

I've heard it in the chillest land -
And on the strangest Sea -
Yet - never - in Extremity,
It asked a crumb - of me.

1. A denotative definition:

Ⓐ is a definition that evokes how the word makes you feel.
Ⓑ is the literal definition of a word.
Ⓒ cannot be found in the dictionary.
Ⓓ is another word for a synonym.

2. A connotative definition:

Ⓐ is a definition that evokes how the word makes you feel.
Ⓑ is the literal definition of a word.
Ⓒ cannot be found in the dictionary.
Ⓓ is another word for a synonym.

3. The tone of a narrator can best be understood by analyzing the

Ⓐ denotation of a word.
Ⓑ connotation of a word.
Ⓒ neither the connotation nor denotation of a word.
Ⓓ None of the above.

Name: ______________________ Date: ______________

4. What is Dickenson comparing hope to in these lines: "Hope" is the thing with feathers -/ That perches in the soul -

5. Determine whether the following statement is True or False.

	True	False
The following quote can best be interpreted as commentary on the power of a storm that can destroy something as strong as hope: And sore must be the storm -/ That could abash the little Bird/ That kept so many warm -	○	○

6. What is the speaker's tone in the following line: "That could abash the little Bird/ That kept so many warm-

Ⓐ Aggressive
Ⓑ Sad
Ⓒ Hopeful
Ⓓ Demanding

7. What is the tone of the lines "And sings the tune without the words -/ And never stops - at all-

Ⓐ Hopeful
Ⓑ Angry
Ⓒ Sad
Ⓓ Mean

8.In the lines, "And sweetest - in the Gale - is heard -/And sore must be the storm", one can define Gale as

Ⓐ War
Ⓑ Storm
Ⓒ Wind
Ⓓ Warning

9.Since hope is given almost human qualities, like "perching", what poetic device is Dickenson using?

10. What do you think the speaker's attitude towards hope is?

Ⓐ She believes deeply in it as something that can help people.
Ⓑ She thinks it is a waste of time because reality is much worse.
Ⓒ She thinks hope is good for other people, but not for her.
Ⓓ All of the above.

Name: ______________________ Date: ______________

Passage 5: Richard Cory

Richard Cory
BY EDWIN ARLINGTON ROBINSON

Whenever Richard Cory went down town,
We people on the pavement looked at him:
He was a gentleman from sole to crown,
Clean favored, and imperially slim.

And he was always quietly arrayed,
And he was always human when he talked;
But still he fluttered pulses when he said,
"Good-morning," and he glittered when he walked.

And he was rich—yes, richer than a king—
And admirably schooled in every grace:
In fine, we thought that he was everything
To make us wish that we were in his place.

So on we worked, and waited for the light,
And went without the meat, and cursed the bread;
And Richard Cory, one calm summer night,
Went home and put a bullet through his head.

1. The structure of a short story tends to follow the following plot diagram:

Ⓐ Exposition, rising action, climax, falling action, resolution.
Ⓑ Rising action, resolution, exposition, climax, falling action.
Ⓒ Character, rising action, exposition, setting, falling action, conflict.
Ⓓ Exposition, character, falling action, rising action, theme.

2. In the poem "Richard Cory", the primary conflict is

Ⓐ Man vs. Man
Ⓑ Man vs. Self
Ⓒ Man vs. Thing
Ⓓ Man vs. Machine

3. What is the climax of the poem? Write the correct answer in the box below.

Ⓐ when Richard walks through town.
Ⓑ when Richard says "Good morning."
Ⓒ when Richard is described as rich.
Ⓓ when Richard shoots himself.

4. Which line best signifies how superior Richard Cory is to the townspeople?

Ⓐ We people on the pavement looked at him:
Ⓑ "Good-morning," and he glittered when he walked.
Ⓒ And he was rich—yes, richer than a king—
Ⓓ All of the above.

5. Describe the tone of the following quote and explain why it is significant.

And Richard Cory, one calm summer night,/ Went home and put a bullet through his head.

6.Determine whether the following statement is True or False.

The townspeople are jealous of Richard Cory.

Ⓐ True
Ⓑ False

7. Determine whether the following statement is True or False.

The writer uses irony in this poem.

Ⓐ True
Ⓑ False

8. Where is parallel plot evident?

Ⓐ When the townspeople are going about their business and Richard shoots himself.
Ⓑ When Richard says hello to the townspeople.
Ⓒ When Richard walks into town.
Ⓓ None of the above.

9. Determine whether the following statement is True or False.

The speaker is a member of the community.

Ⓐ True
Ⓑ False

10. What literary device does the Speaker use when he says: "And went without the meat, and cursed the bread":

Ⓐ Mood
Ⓑ Foreshadowing
Ⓒ Alliteration
Ⓓ Symbolism

Name: ______________________ Date: ______________

Passage 6: Freedom

Freedom

Freedom from fear is the freedom
I claim for you my motherland!
Freedom from the burden of the ages, bending your head,
breaking your back, blinding your eyes to the beckoning
call of the future;
Freedom from the shackles of slumber wherewith
you fasten yourself in night's stillness,
mistrusting the star that speaks of truth's adventurous paths;
freedom from the anarchy of destiny
whole sails are weakly yielded to the blind uncertain winds,
and the helm to a hand ever rigid and cold as death.
Freedom from the insult of dwelling in a puppet's world,
where movements are started through brainless wires,
repeated through mindless habits,
where figures wait with patience and obedience for the
master of show,
to be stirred into a mimicry of life.

1.The point of view of the poem "Freedom" can best be described as:

Ⓐ first-person
Ⓑ second-person
Ⓒ third-person objective
Ⓓ third-person limited
Ⓔ third-person omniscient

2. Matching Column on Point of view

	First-Person	Second-Person	Third-Person Objective	Third-Person	Third-Person Omniscient
When the narrator speaks directly to the reader using you frequently	○	○	○	○	○
When the narrator uses he or she to tell the story and reveals the inner motivations of two or more characters	○	○	○	○	○
When the narrator uses he or she to tell the story but can only reveal one characters thoughts and feelings	○	○	○	○	○
When the story is narrated by "I"	○	○	○	○	○
When the narrator uses he or she to tell the story but doesn't reveal the inner motivations of the characters	○	○	○	○	○

3.This poem can best be described as:

Ⓐ A call to wake up and demand freedom.
Ⓑ A call to revolt against the government.
Ⓒ A plea to his people to remain stoic in the face of tyranny.
Ⓓ A comment on how lonely the people of his country are.

4. When the narrator describes the state of his people as: "shackles of slumber where with/ you fasten yourself in night's stillness", he is using _________to describe the state of the people

Ⓐ personification
Ⓑ simile
Ⓒ metaphor
Ⓓ theme

5. The narrator of the poem demands freedom from the following. Write the correct answer in the box below.

Ⓐ from fear
Ⓑ from shackles of slumber
Ⓒ from the anarchy of destiny
Ⓓ all of the above

6.The narrator uses harsh language to convince his people to wake up and do something. Identify one line where he indicates that his people are passive.

7. What is the importance of reading literature from around the world?

Ⓐ To understand the perspective of someone living in another part of the world.
Ⓑ To understand the struggles of people and how we are all connected.
Ⓒ To learn about the world and different cultures.
Ⓓ All of the above.

8. Select whether the following statement is true or false.

The speaker of the poem is disappointed by his country.

Ⓐ True
Ⓑ False

9.Who do you think the "master of show" is?

Ⓐ The ruling government
Ⓑ The people
Ⓒ The animals
Ⓓ The Americans

10. Select whether the following statement is true or false.

Reading about another culture is a waste of time because you're never going to use that knowledge.

Ⓐ True
Ⓑ False

Passage 7: All The World's A Stage

All the world's a stage,
And all the men and women merely players;
They have their exits and their entrances;
And one man in his time plays many parts,
His acts being seven ages. At first the infant,
Mewling and puking in the nurse's arms;
And then the whining school-boy, with his satchel
And shining morning face, creeping like snail
Unwillingly to school. And then the lover,
Sighing like furnace, with a woeful ballad
Made to his mistress' eyebrow. Then a soldier,
Full of strange oaths, and bearded like the pard,
Jealous in honour, sudden and quick in quarrel,
Seeking the bubble reputation
Even in the cannon's mouth. And then the justice,
In fair round belly with good capon lin'd,
With eyes severe and beard of formal cut,
Full of wise saws and modern instances;
And so he plays his part. The sixth age shifts
Into the lean and slipper'd pantaloon,
With spectacles on nose and pouch on side;

Name: ______________________ Date: ______________

His youthful hose, well sav'd, a world too wide
For his shrunk shank; and his big manly voice,
Turning again toward childish treble, pipes
And whistles in his sound. Last scene of all,
That ends this strange eventful history,
Is second childishness and mere oblivion;
Sans teeth, sans eyes, sans taste, sans everything.

1.In the poem, the narrator addresses the 7 stages of man. Of the following, Which of the following stages are not identified?

Ⓐ Infant
Ⓑ Schoolboy
Ⓒ Lover
Ⓓ Soldier
Ⓔ Enemy

2. In the poem, the narrator describes the world as a stage and mankind as many parts. What can you infer the narrator feels about mankind?

Ⓐ That the world is full of people who are all the same and all dependent on each other.
Ⓑ That a man's life is beautiful and demands recognition.
Ⓒ Mankind is marked by amazing stages, with each stage being a unique experience.
Ⓓ People are all different and unique.

3. In the painting, the artist captures these 7 stages of man as well. Some images and stages have been brought to the foreground of the painting and stand out more. Which stage is represented by the character in the green jacket carrying what looks to be a box?

Ⓐ And then the whining school-boy, with his satchel/ And shining morning face.
Ⓑ And then the justice /In fair round belly with good capon lin'd,/ With eyes severe and beard of formal cut.
Ⓒ At first the infant / Mewling and puking in the nurse's arms.
Ⓓ Is second childishness and mere oblivion.

Name: ______________________ Date: ______________

4.In the painting, there are images that make the "world" depicted in the poem seem almost like:

Ⓐ A party
Ⓑ A circus
Ⓒ A happy street scene
Ⓓ A dog park

5. The word "reminiscence" means a story told about a past event remembered by the narrator and it is printed on the bottom of the image. How is the poem "All the World's a Stage" similar? Which of the following is true based on what we can gather from the poem?

Ⓐ The poem and the picture are not alike because the poem is not a memory.
Ⓑ The poem is about a past event as the narrator's life closes.
Ⓒ The poem captures the stages of man almost as a memory; looking around and back at the various points in one's life.
Ⓓ All of the above.

6. In both the painting and the poem, the stages of man appear:

Ⓐ Separate and comical
Ⓑ United and sad
Ⓒ Separate and sad
Ⓓ United and comical
Ⓔ None of the above

7. In the background of the painting, there is a boy on stilts doffing his hat. Which line in the poem does that refer to? Write the correct answer in the box given below.

Ⓐ And then the whining school-boy, with his satchel
Ⓑ "And then the lover,/ Sighing like furnace, with a woeful ballad/ Made to his mistress' eyebrow."
Ⓒ At first the infant / Mewling and puking in the nurse's arms
Ⓓ In second childishness and mere oblivion/Sans teeth, sans eyes, sans taste, sans every thing
Ⓔ None of the above

Name: ________________________ Date: ______________

8. What theme is depicted by both the painting and the poem?

9. If you had to choose, which medium - the painting or the poem, does a better job of depicting the idea that "all the world's a stage"? Explain why in 3 sentences.

10. The narrator writes "All the world's a stage/ And all the men and women merely players".

Based on your observations in both the poem and painting, what do you think that the word **players** means?

Ⓐ Actors
Ⓑ Children
Ⓒ Directors
Ⓓ Gods

Name: ______________________ Date: ______________

Passage 8: The Three Little Pigs

It was a time of space travel, and the three little pigs were getting ready to take off. They knew they had to have the best shuttle around. There were many enemies in this distant land, and rumor has it some had very big teeth and lots of hair. The first little pig decided to build his space shuttle out of fiberglass because it was cheap and readily available. Unfortunately for him, the enemies knew exactly how to destroy that shuttle and it took one huff and puff to send that little pig crashing back to earth. (written by Fran Havard)

1. In the excerpt, what elements have been adapted from the classic fairy tale "The Three Little Pigs"?

Ⓐ Character
Ⓑ Theme
Ⓒ Antagonist
Ⓓ All of the Above

2. What words does the writer use in the excerpt, to highlight the wolf?

3. In the original tale of The Three Little Pigs, the writer uses hay to build the first house. How is it different in this futuristic version?

4.In this version of The Three Little Pigs, the crucial difference in the adaptation is in the _______.

Ⓐ Setting
Ⓑ Character
Ⓒ Theme
Ⓓ Symbolism
Ⓔ None of the above

5. You've decided to write a short story based on the story of Hansel and Gretel but you want to change Hansel and Gretel into two orphans living in NYC in 2011. Which detail are you least likely to borrow from the original tale? Write the correct answer in the box below.

Ⓐ The breadcrumbs
Ⓑ The witch
Ⓒ The house made of candy
Ⓓ The lumberjack
Ⓔ All of the above

READING: INFORMATIONAL TEXT

Passage 1: Lower the Voting Age

When we think about the minimum age for voting, the first question that comes to our mind is: How young is too young? The minimum ages vary in the different contexts such as that for driving, marriage, joining the army, and so on. While there is an argument that 16 and 17-year olds are too immature to vote, there is also a danger that they might not vote at all.

When we look at the trends in voting turnout, it is a bit distressing to note the numbers. This disenchantment of the young towards voting is a matter of concern as voting is a habit and it is necessary to ensure that this habit is inculcated as soon as possible. If left unattended, it could lead to ever lower participation rates in the decades to come, questioning the legitimacy of governments in a vicious spiral in which the poor voting turnout results in skepticism towards democracy, and vice versa.

The causes of disillusionment are many. The young adults look at voting as a privilege or choice rather than duty. The politically active persons tend to campaign on single issues and matters of concern rather than for a particular party. Politicians also focus and woo the older voters rather than the young as they are more likely to vote.

There are some countries which have made voting compulsory thereby increasing turnout rates. But this is not a solution to the disillusionment. Governments have to focus on ways to rekindle the passion, rather than continue to ignore the absence of it. A good step would be to lower the voting age to 16. This would ensure that new voters get off to the best possible start.

This cannot be considered as an arbitrary change. The current age for voting, which is 18 coincides with finishing compulsory education and leaving home. Away from their parents, they have no established voters to follow as they have limited connection to their new communities. In this process, they remain away from the electoral roll, and the habit of voting is not established. If the voting age is 16 years, they can get into the habit of voting by accompanying their parents to polling stations.

However, just lowering the voting age alone will not help. Schools can contribute to better turnouts by helping the children register. Governments also need to put more effort at keeping electoral rolls current. Civics lessons can be improved. Schools can also have courses that promote open debate thereby giving the pupils a chance to vote in aspects of their school. This will boost political commitment later in life.

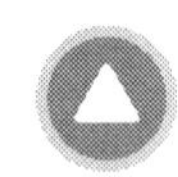

A lower voting age would strengthen the voice of the young and also signal that their opinions matter. They, as future citizens would be the ones who would be facing issues such as climate change, pensions, and healthcare, etc. in the future.

1. Implicit reading forces the reader to

Ⓐ Read between the lines and determine the purpose of the writer's work.
Ⓑ Use context clues to understand what words mean.
Ⓒ Make inferences based on the reasoning present.
Ⓓ All of the above.

2. Ms. Havard walked into her children's room and started yelling at them about making messes. She decided she had enough of cleaning up after them. While yelling at them, her youngest daughter, Evie, started crying, and ran underneath her bedcovers.

Which sentence reveals explicitly Ms. Havard's feelings?

Ⓐ While yelling at them, her youngest daughter, Evie, started crying.
Ⓑ She decided she had enough of cleaning up after them.
Ⓒ Ms. Havard walked into her children's room and started yelling at them.
Ⓓ All of the above.

3. Ms. Havard walked into her children's room and started yelling at them about making messes. She decided she had enough of cleaning up after them. While yelling at them, her youngest daughter, Evie, started crying, and ran underneath her bedcovers. Lillian, the oldest, started cleaning up right away.

If you implicitly read this, you might ascertain that:

Ⓐ Ms. Havard has cleaned up after their messes multiple times.
Ⓑ Ms. Havard is a terrible mom.
Ⓒ Ms. Havard needs to hire a maid.
Ⓓ Ms. Havard loves her children very much.

Name: ______________________ Date: ______________

4. Ms. Havard walked into her children's room and started yelling at them about making messes. She decided she had enough of cleaning up after them. While yelling at them, her youngest daughter, Evie, started crying, and ran underneath her bedcovers. Lillian, the oldest, started cleaning up right away.

If you implicitly read this, you might ascertain that:

Ⓐ Lillian doesn't know how to behave.
Ⓑ Lillian is more sensitive than Evie.
Ⓒ Evie is more sensitive than Lillian
Ⓓ Evie's brother, Oliver was mean to her.

5. In the nonfiction article, "Lowering the Voting Age" the author uses which of the following points to support her argument?

Ⓐ After a child turns 18, they are usually no longer with their parents in the home, and won't have the right modeling to vote.
Ⓑ Schools should be helping to enroll children in voter registration and at 18, these students are no longer in schools.
Ⓒ Lowering the voting age would give young people a voice in their communities.
Ⓓ All of the above.

6. In which paragraph(s) does the author provide evidence that supports the effectiveness of lowering the voting age? Write the answer in the box given below.

Ⓐ In paragraph 2
Ⓑ In paragraph 3
Ⓒ In the conclusion
Ⓓ She offers none

Name: ______________________ Date: ______________

7. How can the writer improve their concluding paragraph?

Ⓐ It's perfect the way it is.
Ⓑ She should recap the main points of her argument in the conclusion.
Ⓒ She should use better punctuation.
Ⓓ She needs to write at least 8 more sentences.

8. Which sentence in paragraph 1 best illustrates the author's thesis?

9. After reading this article, what conclusions can you make about the author's opinion on lowering the voting age?

10. Determine whether the following statement is True or False.

	True	False
Evidence and reasoning are the same things in an argumentative essay.	○	○

Name: ______________________ Date: ______________

Passage 2: Baseball

Every country has a National game. Just as cricket is the national game of England, baseball can be termed as the national game of America. Baseball became widely popular after the Civil war, and it was introduced to all parts of the country. The soldiers learned the game in their camp. Today, every village and town has its own baseball team, and the interest in the game is general. The baseball is a game for the youth, and it is not meant for men who are middle-aged, unlike golf. The chances are that if a man plays baseball in his youth, he is most likely to stay interested in the game throughout his life. Baseball requires a lot of skill. Baseball does not provide as much exercise or physical activity as tennis or football. Baseball may not be conducted with a very high regard for sportsman spirit, but the American public is captivated by it, and winning of championship series in the professional league is a celebrated national event.

A baseball team consists of nine players. The various positions of the game are the pitcher, first base, catcher, second and third base, shortstop. These are called the in-field, right-field, left and centre-field, and left-field. The position of an umpire in the baseball game is of utmost importance and his verdict on the game can result in either victory or a defeat for the playing teams. Hence, it is very important for the umpire to know the rules of the game very well and he should be impartial to both the teams. The umpire should be fair in all decisions and should stick to his decision even if the entire team opposes his decision by "kicking." The cause of rowdyism in baseball is mainly due to this cause. It is important for a good player to show himself as a gentleman, whatever may be the circumstance.

Like in any other game, winning becomes the most important thing in baseball which results in a desire to score higher than the opponent becomes more important than fair play or focus on the real benefits of the game. In fact, most of the clean-cut games are played by school and college teams, and these are mostly amateurs.

1. What is the main idea of the essay?

Ⓐ How baseball compares to cricket
Ⓑ The poor behavior of baseball players
Ⓒ Why baseball is an inferior sport
Ⓓ All about baseball

Name: ______________________ Date: ______________

2. Locate the mistake the writer makes in the following sentence in paragraph 2.

Every boy knows that a baseball team consists of nine players:

Ⓐ Generalizes all boys.
Ⓑ Makes baseball seem like every boy has to play it and know.
Ⓒ All of the above.
Ⓓ None of the above.

3. In paragraph 2, the writer spends too much time describing. Write your answer in the box below .

Ⓐ The players
Ⓑ The umpire's role
Ⓒ The game
Ⓓ Cricket

4. What are the weaknesses of the conclusion?________

5. What does the writer fail to include in the second paragraph?

Ⓐ A clincher
Ⓑ A topic sentence
Ⓒ Proper punctuation
Ⓓ None of the above

6. What are the problems with the introduction?

Ⓐ Too many ideas
Ⓑ No thesis
Ⓒ No clear, general opening sentence
Ⓓ All of the above

7. Which of the following sentences about summarizing is true?

Ⓐ Summarizing teaches the students to isolate what is important.
Ⓑ Summarizing is retelling.
Ⓒ Summarizing helps the student to demonstrate an understanding of the text.
Ⓓ All of the above.

Name: ______________________ Date: ______________

Passage 3: Effects Of Video Games

Video games have become an inescapable part of growing up and one cannot be wrong when we say that they also play a large part of the development and socialization of children. Pokemon which was very popular has grown from just a video game into a cultural phenomenon. Technology has become more pervasive in everyday life, and with that comes the question Is technology doing good for us? The effects of video games have always been a cause of contention, right from the time they were invented. Parents have opined that video games cause children to socially isolate themselves, has been a cause of obesity, made children insensitive to violence, and in short a waste of time. However, when we look at the wide variety of games available to play, it becomes hard to decide if all video games are bad for you in general. But there is enough evidence for both arguments; video games can be both good and bad for those that play them.

1. What is the purpose of the essay?

Ⓐ To explain why video games are bad.
Ⓑ To explain why video games are good.
Ⓒ To present a balanced view of the positives and negatives of video games.
Ⓓ To explain why teenagers shouldn't play video games.

2. Why does the writer introduce Pokemon into the opening of her argument?

Ⓐ To emphasize positively how this video game made a culture bond.
Ⓑ To emphasize how dangerous Pokemon is for our culture.
Ⓒ To introduce the idea of how boring video games are.
Ⓓ None of the above.

3. What are three reasons the writer gives for parents disliking video games?

Name: ______________________ Date: ______________

4. **Since the following sentence sums up the author's main purpose of the essay, "But there is enough evidence for both arguments; video games can be both good and bad for those that play them." This sentence is called the:**

5. **Identify the most important piece of evidence that you think the writer uses to support his argument for video games. Explain why you think the evidence is effective?**

6. **Match the quote to the type of argument you think it is**

	Informative	Persuasive	Descriptive
Come down to Bill's Auto and get your red hot deal today	○	○	○
Today the average person eats his/her weight in sugar every year	○	○	○
The dark house stood aloof and lonely at the edge of a crumbling hillside.	○	○	○

7. The writer's conclusion contains which idea?

Ⓐ Video games can be a very bad thing.
Ⓑ One should minimize the amount of time spent playing a video game and go outside instead.
Ⓒ Video games should be chosen wisely and played sparingly.
Ⓓ Video games are good for you, and it's unnecessary to manage the time spent playing them.

8. How does a writer create a mood?

Ⓐ Through a description of setting
Ⓑ Through a description of characters
Ⓒ Through sentence structure
Ⓓ All of the above

9. In the following sentence, how does the writer create a mood?

"The dark house stood aloof and lonely at the edge of a crumbling hillside."

Ⓐ She uses personification to bring the spooky house to life.
Ⓑ She describes the setting.
Ⓒ She uses words like dark and aloof to enhance the spooky mood.
Ⓓ All of the above.

10. To structure one's argument, one must follow this simple paragraph structure. Place your answers in the box below

Ⓐ Supporting sentence #2
Ⓑ Supporting sentence #1
Ⓒ Topic sentence
Ⓓ Clincher
Ⓔ Supporting sentence #3

Name: ______________________ Date: ______________

Passage 4: Patrick Henry Speech (March 23, 1775)

They tell us, sir, that we are weak; unable to cope with so formidable an adversary. But when shall we be stronger? Will it be the next week or the next year? Will it be when we are totally disarmed, and when a British guard shall be stationed in every house? Shall we gather strength by irresolution and inaction? Shall we acquire the means of effectual resistance by lying supinely on our backs and hugging the delusive phantom of hope, until our enemies shall have bound us hand and foot? Sir, we are not weak if we make a proper use of those means which the God of nature hath placed in our power. The millions of people, armed in the holy cause of liberty, and in such a country as that which we possess, are invincible by any force which our enemy can send against us. Besides, sir, we shall not fight our battles alone. There is a just God who presides over the destinies of nations, and who will raise up friends to fight our battles for us. The battle, sir, is not to the strong alone; it is to the vigilant, the active, the brave. Besides, sir, we have no election. If we were base enough to desire it, it is now too late to retire from the contest. There is no retreat but in submission and slavery! Our chains are forged! Their clanking may be heard on the plains of Boston! The war is inevitable—and let it come! I repeat it, sir, let it come.

It is in vain, sir, to extenuate the matter. Gentlemen may cry, Peace, Peace—but there is no peace. The war is actually begun! The next gale that sweeps from the north will bring to our ears the clash of resounding arms! Our brethren are already in the field! Why stand we here idle? What is it that gentlemen wish? What would they have? Is life so dear, or peace so sweet, as to be purchased at the price of chains and slavery? Forbid it, Almighty God! I know not what course others may take; but as for me, give me liberty or give me death!

1.In the opening line of Paragraph 1, Henry uses the word "formidable" to describe his enemy, Great Britan. Based on the context of the word, what can you assume that "formidable" means?

Ⓐ Impressively large and powerful
Ⓑ Mean
Ⓒ Aggressive
Ⓓ Not worthy of one's time

2. Henry uses ______________ in the lines "Shall we acquire the means of effectual resistance by lying supinely on our backs and hugging the delusive phantom of hope" because it's clear he doesn't mean they should lie down on their backs and hang onto hope.

Ⓐ sarcasm
Ⓑ direct speech
Ⓒ a simile
Ⓓ a declaractive statement

3. The series of questions that he asks the audience, most ardently reflect his desire for the colonial people to be:

Ⓐ Weak and docile
Ⓑ Angry and revolutionary
Ⓒ Strong but passive
Ⓓ Brave and stoic

4. The quote, "Is life so dear, or peace so sweet, as to be purchased at the price of chains and slavery?" uses imagery to compare freedom to remaining under British rule. Which type of imagery does he use?

Ⓐ Simile
Ⓑ Metaphor
Ⓒ Onomatopoeia
Ⓓ Assonance

5. What is the effect of his closing line changing from a series of questions to emphatic exclamation marks: "Forbid it, Almighty God! I know not what course others may take; but as for me, give me liberty or give me death!"

Ⓐ He stops questioning the people and emphatically demands that his answer is death over the slavery to the British people
Ⓑ The exclamations highlight how angry he is getting by the end of the speech.
Ⓒ Both of the above
Ⓓ None of the above

6. What rhetorical device does Henry use in this quote: "There is no retreat but in sub mission and slavery! Our chains are forged! Their clanking may be heard on the plains of Boston!"

Ⓐ Metaphor and hyperbole
Ⓑ Hyperbole and personification
Ⓒ Hyperbole only
Ⓓ A and B

Name: ______________________ Date: ______________

7. In no more than 2 words, mention what the tone of this article is.

8. ___________ language is language that involves a figure of speech. Write your answer in the box given below

9. A word that suggests a secondary or shade of meaning is _______________.Write your answer in the box given below

10. Select the correct term that matches the definition below.

	figurative	connotative	tone
The attitude of the speaker as understood through the writer's syntax, word choice, etc.	○	○	○

11. In the box below, write the term that matches the following definition.

Appeals to the reasoning or logical argument making

12. Select the term that best matches the definition in the table below.

	Ethos	Logos	Pathos
Appeals to the audience's heart	◯	◯	◯

13. Select the term that best matches the definition below.

Emphasizes the credibility of the persuader or the speaker

Ⓐ Ethos
Ⓑ Logos
Ⓒ Pathos
Ⓓ None of the above

14. Patrick Henry's argument can best be described as (ethos, logos or pathos)

____

15. Which two types of rhetoric are used in the following lines?

"Forbid it, Almighty God! I know not what course others may take; but as for me, give me liberty or give me death!

Ⓐ Ethos and pathos
Ⓑ Pathos and logos
Ⓒ Logos and ethos
Ⓓ None of the above

Name: ____________________ Date: ____________

16. Which rhetorical device does Patrick Henry use in the following line? Write your answer in the box below.

"Shall we gather strength by irresolution and inaction?"

Ⓐ Rhetorical questions
Ⓑ Rhetorical answers
Ⓒ Sarcasm
Ⓓ Amplification

Passage 5: John F Kennedy
John F Kennedy's inaugural address in 1961

Vice President Johnson, Mr. Speaker, Mr. Chief Justice, President Eisenhower, Vice President Nixon, President Truman, Reverend Clergy, fellow citizens:

We observe today not a victory of party but a celebration of freedom--symbolizing an end as well as a beginning--signifying renewal as well as change. For I have sworn before you and Almighty God the same solemn oath our forbears prescribed nearly a century and three-quarters ago.

The world is very different now. For man holds in his mortal hands the power to abolish all forms of human poverty and all forms of human life. And yet the same revolutionary beliefs for which our forebears fought are still at issue around the globe--the belief that the rights of man come not from the generosity of the state but from the hand of God.

We dare not forget today that we are the heirs of that first revolution. Let the word go forth from this time and place, to friend and foe alike, that the torch has been passed to a new generation of Americans--born in this century, tempered by war, disciplined by a hard and bitter peace, proud of our ancient heritage--and unwilling to witness or permit the slow undoing of those human rights to which this nation has always been committed, and to which we are committed today at home and around the world.

Let every nation know, whether it wishes us well or ill, that we shall pay any price, bear any burden, meet any hardship, support any friend, oppose any foe to assure the survival and the success of liberty.

This much we pledge--and more.

To those old allies whose cultural and spiritual origins we share, we pledge the loyalty of faithful friends. United there is little we cannot do in a host of cooperative ventures. Divided there is little we can do--for we dare not meet a powerful challenge at odds and split asunder.

To those new states whom we welcome to the ranks of the free, we pledge our word that one form of colonial control shall not have passed away merely to be replaced by a far more iron tyranny. We shall not always expect to find them supporting our view. But we shall always hope to find them strongly supporting their own freedom--and to remember that, in the past, those who foolishly sought power by riding the back of the tiger ended up inside.

To those people in the huts and villages of half the globe struggling to break the bonds of mass misery, we pledge our best efforts to help them help themselves, for whatever period is required--not because the communists may be doing it, not because we seek their votes, but because it is right. If a free society cannot help the many who are poor, it cannot save the few who are rich.

To our sister republics south of our border, we offer a special pledge--to convert our good words into good deeds--in a new alliance for progress--to assist free men and free governments in casting off the chains of poverty. But this peaceful revolution of hope cannot become the prey of hostile powers. Let all our neighbors know that we shall join with them to oppose aggression or subversion anywhere in the Americas. And let every other power know that this Hemisphere intends to remain the master of its own house.

To that world assembly of sovereign states, the United Nations, our last best hope in an age where the instruments of war have far outpaced the instruments of peace, we renew our pledge of support--to prevent it from becoming merely a forum for invective--to strengthen its shield of the new and the weak--and to enlarge the area in which its writ may run.

Finally, to those nations who would make themselves our adversary, we offer not a pledge but a request: that both sides begin anew the quest for peace before the dark powers of destruction unleashed by science engulf all humanity in planned or accidental self-destruction.

We dare not tempt them with weakness. For only when our arms are sufficient beyond doubt can we be certain beyond doubt that they will never be employed.

But neither can two great and powerful groups of nations take comfort from our present course--both sides overburdened by the cost of modern weapons, both rightly alarmed by the steady spread of the deadly atom, yet both racing to alter that uncertain balance of terror that stays the hand of mankind's final war.

So let us begin anew--remembering on both sides that civility is not a sign of weakness, and sincerity is always subject to proof. Let us never negotiate out of fear. But let us never fear to negotiate.

Let both sides explore what problems unite us instead of belaboring those problems which divide us.

Let both sides, for the first time, formulate serious and precise proposals for the inspection and control of arms--and bring the absolute power to destroy other nations under the absolute control of all nations.

Let both sides seek to invoke the wonders of science instead of its terrors. Together let us explore the stars, conquer the deserts, eradicate disease, tap the ocean depths and encourage the arts and commerce.

Let both sides unite to heed in all corners of the earth the command of Isaiah--to "undo the heavy burdens . . . (and) let the oppressed go free."

And if a beachhead of cooperation may push back the jungle of suspicion, let both sides join in creating a new endeavor, not a new balance of power, but a new world of law, where the strong are just and the weak secure and the peace preserved.

All this will not be finished in the first one hundred days. Nor will it be finished in the first one thousand days, nor in the life of this Administration, nor even perhaps in our lifetime on this planet. But let us begin.

In your hands, my fellow citizens, more than mine, will rest the final success or failure of our course. Since this country was founded, each generation of Americans has been summoned to give testimony to its national loyalty. The graves of young Americans who answered the call to service surround the globe.

Now the trumpet summons us again--not as a call to bear arms, though arms we need--not as a call to battle, though embattled we are-- but a call to bear the burden of a long twilight struggle, year in and year out, "rejoicing in hope, patient in tribulation"--a struggle against the common enemies of man: tyranny, poverty, disease, and war itself.

Can we forge against these enemies a grand and global alliance, North and South, East and West, that can assure a more fruitful life for all mankind? Will you join in that historic effort?

In the long history of the world, only a few generations have been granted the role of defending freedom in its hour of maximum danger. I do not shrink from this responsibility--I welcome it. I do not believe that any of us would exchange places with any other people or any other generation. The energy, the faith, the devotion which we bring to this endeavor will light our country and all who serve it--and the glow from that fire can truly light the world.

And so, my fellow Americans: ask not what your country can do for you--ask what you can do for your country.

My fellow citizens of the world: ask not what America will do for you, but what together we can do for the freedom of man.

Finally, whether you are citizens of America or citizens of the world, ask of us here the same high standards of strength and sacrifice which we ask of you. With a good conscience our only sure reward, with history the final judge of our deeds, let us go forth to lead the land we love, asking His blessing and His help but knowing that here on earth God's work must truly be our own.

Name: ______________________ Date: ______________

1. Which figure of speech does Kennedy use in his rhetoric when he says "those who foolishly sought power by riding the back of the tiger ended up inside"?

Ⓐ Metaphor
Ⓑ Overstatement
Ⓒ Irony
Ⓓ Personification

2. Match each statement to the correct figure of speech from Kennedy's rhetoric.

	Personification	Overstatment	Symbol
Let both sides unite to heed in all corners of the earth the command of Isaiah--to "undo the heavy burdens . . . (and) let the oppressed go free.	○	○	○
a celebration of free-dom--symbolizing an end as well as a begin-ning--signifying renewal as well as change.	○	○	○
this Hemisphere intends to remain the master of its own house.	○	○	○

3. What does the sentence "ask not what America will do for you, but what together we can do for the freedom of man", In the rhetoric represent?

Ⓐ Personification
Ⓑ Synecdoche
Ⓒ Irony
Ⓓ Simile

4. A rhetorical device in which the speaker greatly exaggerates to make a point is called

Ⓐ Hyperbole
Ⓑ Alliteration
Ⓒ Assonance
Ⓓ Metaphor

5. In the opening line of this excerpt, John F Kennedy says "We observe today not a victory of party but a celebration of freedom--symbolizing an end as well as a beginning--signifying renewal as well as change." Who is Kennedy referring to when he says "we"?

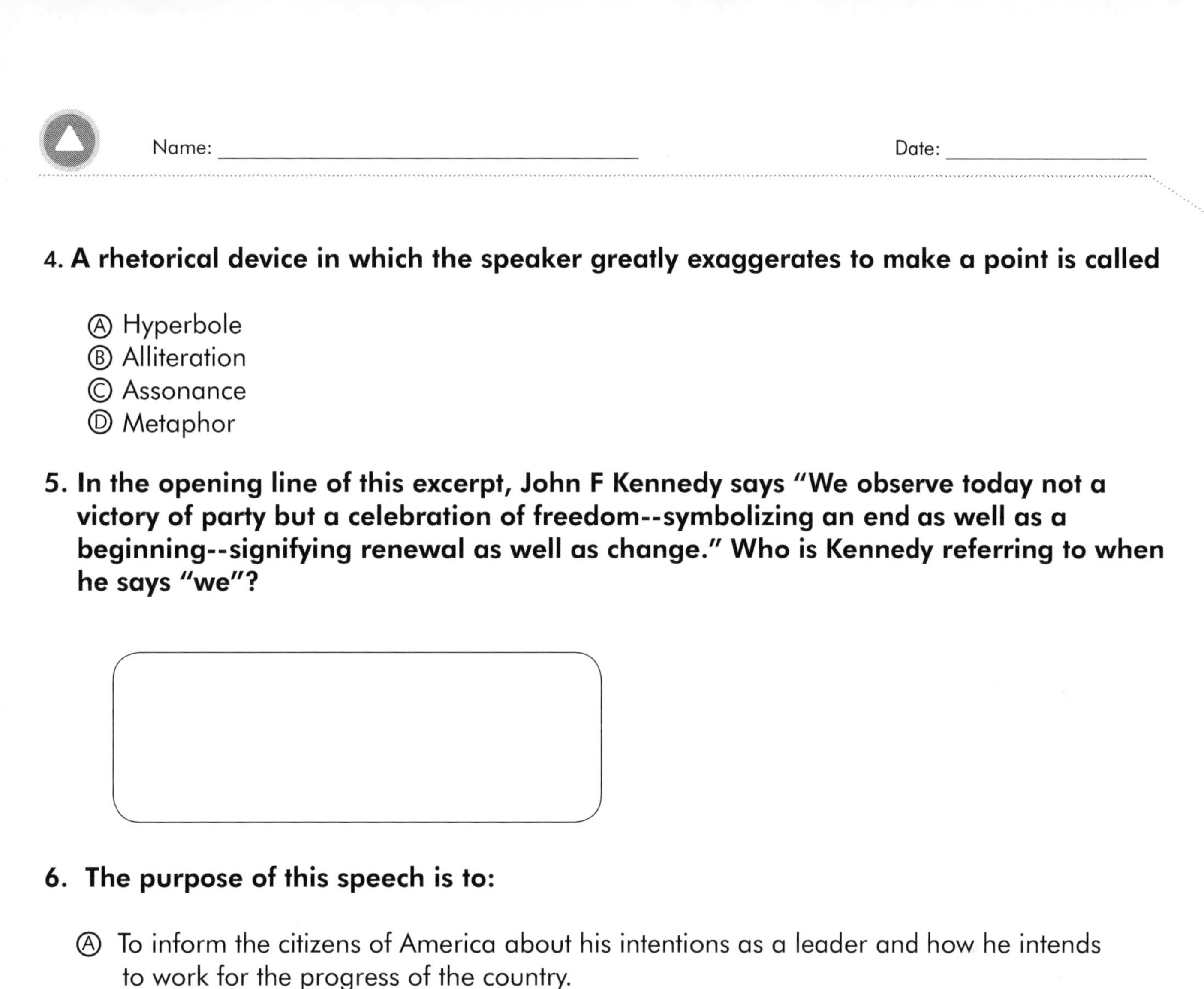

6. The purpose of this speech is to:

Ⓐ To inform the citizens of America about his intentions as a leader and how he intends to work for the progress of the country.
Ⓑ Emphasize his anger at the war and its effects.
Ⓒ Question the countrymen about their role and duties.
Ⓓ None of the above.

7. The theme(s) of Kennedy's speech is, write your answer in the box below .

Ⓐ Strength
Ⓑ Compassion
Ⓒ Hope and belief
Ⓓ All of the above

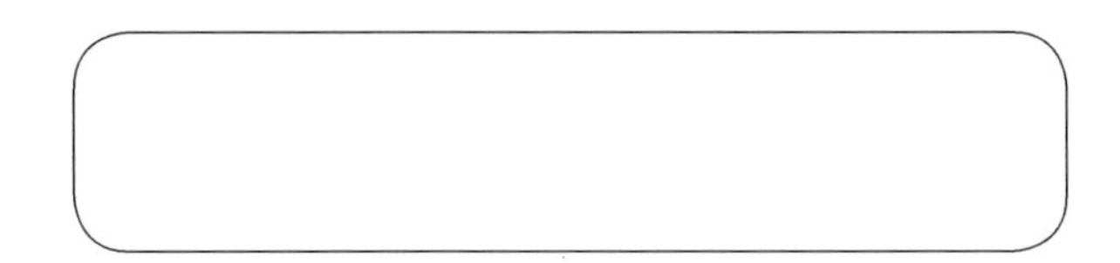

8. What does Kennedy mean when he says: "ask not what your country can do for you--ask what you can do for your country"? Elaborate with specific details from the passage and your thoughts about the statement.

9. After reading the speech, what do you understand about the situation in the world at the time of the address?

Name: ______________________ Date: ______________

Passage 6: President Lincoln Speech

President Lincoln delivered the 272 words Gettysburg Address on November 19, 1863, on the battlefield near Gettysburg, Pennsylvania. It was written during the civil war between the North and the South of a much divided America.

"Fourscore and seven years ago our fathers brought forth, on this continent, a new nation, conceived in liberty, and dedicated to the proposition that all men are created equal. Now we are engaged in a great civil war, testing whether that nation, or any nation so conceived, and so dedicated, can long endure. We are met on a great battle-field of that war. We have come to dedicate a portion of that field, as a final resting-place for those who here gave their lives, that that nation might live. It is altogether fitting and proper that we should do this. But, in a larger sense, we cannot dedicate, we cannot consecrate—we cannot hallow—this ground. The brave men, living and dead, who struggled here, have consecrated it far above our poor power to add or detract.

1. The purpose of this speech is to:

Ⓐ Respectfully dedicate a portion of the ground for the soldiers who have died in battle.
Ⓑ Emphasize Lincoln's anger at the American people.
Ⓒ Question whether or not America is going to make it or if it will self-destruct.
Ⓓ Both B. and C.

2. The tone of Lincoln's speech is:

Ⓐ Happy
Ⓑ Worried
Ⓒ Respectful
Ⓓ B and C only

3. What does Lincoln mean when he says: "The brave men, living and dead, who struggled here, have consecrated it far above our poor power to add or detract."

Ⓐ The men who fought for their country already made the ground sacred just by their actions in war alone.
Ⓑ The soldiers that died blessed the land.
Ⓒ Those listening to the address are making no attempt to respect these soldiers.
Ⓓ None of the above.

4. Determine whether the following statement is True or False.

A primary source isn't as reliable as a secondary source.

Ⓐ True
Ⓑ False

5. Determine whether the following statement in the table is True or False.

	True	False
"The Gettysburg Address" is an example of a primary source.	◯	◯

Name: ______________________ Date: ______________

Passage 7: Can bullying be overcome by Kindness

Being Kind is not easy. In fact, it is very complex. If kindness had been a simple behavioral trait, then everyone would have been kind, and no one would have experienced meanness or bullying. A world in which Kindness is the norm is an ideal world. When we ask if it is possible to have homes, schools, communities where Kindness is the norm, the answer would be Yes. However to do so, we need to teach, model, and reward kindness.

For being kind, one needs to think about the needs and concerns of others. Inculcating the behavior of volunteering to help others and work for that affect their communities helps in developing Kindness and empathy. Compassionate thinking and generous actions demonstrate kindness.

Unfortunately, in many schools, negative behaviors such as bullying results in punishment which is thought to reduce this kind of behaviour in future. On the contrary, research shows that for "zero-tolerance" and to end bullying and violence punishment-based approaches do not work. Given this knowledge, it makes better sense to focus on teaching and modeling behaviors such as kindness and empathy.

Ways to Teach Kindness

• Mindfulness involves becoming aware of the specific thought, emotion, or behavior. This means that by being mentally flexible, and through training, even young children can learn kindness.

• Social-Emotional Learning (SEL) teaches kindness by focusing on cooperation, responsibility, self-control, empathy, and provides specific actions to build these skills.

• Acts of Kindness are actions such as doing something nice to others. Doing acts of kindness cause positive ripple effects to those who experience and witness kindness.

Impact of Teaching Kindness

Elementary school students who performed three acts of kindness per week saw that they were significantly more accepted by their peers compared to kids who did not perform three kind acts of kindness. Students who are taught kindness are more empathic, more socially aware, and connected. They also receive higher grades. Be kind—it is free, and the payback is good for all!

Name: ______________________ Date: ______________

1.Logical flaws in an argument are called logical...

Ⓐ Mistakes
Ⓑ Fallacies
Ⓒ Errors
Ⓓ Buttons

2. An example of a logical fallacy is

Ⓐ Begging the question
Ⓑ Slippery slope
Ⓒ Straw man
Ⓓ All of the above

3. This type of logical fallacy, can best be defined as: I didn't remember to take out the trash, so now it is going to be out there all week. MY next door neighbors will get angry at the smell of it and probably start a campaign to kick me out of here. Write your answer in the box given below .

Ⓐ Begging the question
Ⓑ Slippery slope
Ⓒ Straw man
Ⓓ Ad hominem

4. The flaw in this argument is: "Students who are taught kindness are more empathic, more socially aware and connected. They also receive higher grades."

Ⓐ Begging the question
Ⓑ Slippery slope
Ⓒ Straw man
Ⓓ Ad hominem

5. In argument making, one often has to recognize the counter argument. An example of counterargument in the essay can be found in which line? Is it effective and why?

6. What is one way the writer identifies to teach kindness?

7. Determine whether the following statement is True or False.

	True	False
The writer's thesis can be found in the introduction: "However to do so, we need to teach, model and reward kindness."	○	○

8. Write the correct term that matches the definition in the box below.

Making an argument, but drawing conclusions and not fully supporting those conclusions

9. Write the correct term that matches the definition in the box below.

Attack a person to make an argument

10. Select the correct term that matches the definition below.

	Hasty generalization	Ad hominem	Straw man
When one side of the argument is presented as so extreme, you just can't agree with it	○	○	○

Name: ______________________ Date: ______________

Language Standards

Lesson1: Grammar and Usage

1. Which phrase represents an adverb phrase in the following sentence: "He placed the present by the birthday cake."

Ⓐ He placed
Ⓑ the present
Ⓒ by the birthday cake
Ⓓ placed the present

2. Which phrase represents an adverb clause in the following sentence: "You can start the oven while I finish making the dough."

Ⓐ You can start
Ⓑ start the oven
Ⓒ making the dough
Ⓓ while I finish making the dough

3. What word is described by the adverb 'extremely' in the following sentence: "The present he purchased for her birthday was extremely expensive."

Ⓐ present
Ⓑ purchased
Ⓒ birthday
Ⓓ expensive

4. Which type of clause is represented in the following sentence? "Humans and insects are similar in that they both need to breathe to survive, and <u>both breathe out carbon dioxide.</u>"Write your answer in the box below.

Ⓐ independent clause
Ⓑ dependent clause
Ⓒ noun clause
Ⓓ relative clause

5. Which type of clause is represented in the following sentence? "Jane's English teacher, who is also in charge of the school yearbook, is retiring next year."

Ⓐ independent clause
Ⓑ adverbial clause
Ⓒ noun clause
Ⓓ relative clause

6. What punctuation should separate the dependent clause from the independent clause in the following sentence? "Starting with Rosa Parks's refusal to sit in the back of the bus the Montgomery bus boycott brought national attention to the issue of segregation."

Ⓐ semicolon (;)
Ⓑ comma (,)
Ⓒ colon (:)
Ⓓ period (.)

7. In his famous Gettysburg Address, President Abraham Lincoln stated, "Government of the people, by the people, for the people, shall not perish from the earth."

List the phrases that demonstrate parallel structure in this statement.

Name: ______________________ Date: ______________

8. Your friend asked for help revising her essay for English class. You notice that many of her sentences are short with a similar structure. Read part of her essay below, then write her a note explaining why she should revise her essay to use a variety of sentence structures. Include an example of a revised sentence she could use in her essay.

"Hamlet is a play written by William Shakespeare. It was written in 1599. It is very famous. The play is about the character Hamlet. Hamlet is the prince of Denmark. Hamlet is upset because his father has died. Hamlet finds out that his uncle killed his father. Hamlet learns about his father's murder from a ghost."

9. Each sentence shows a correct example of parallel structure. In the middle column, write the phrase that is parallel to the underlined phrase(s) in the sentence. In the final column, label the type of phrases that are used to create the parallel structure.

Sentence	Write the phrases	Type of phrases
Siggy enjoys baking cupcakes and watching movies.		
That celebrity is famous for her brilliant acting and sensational dancing.		
Darlene looked for her lost kitten under the couch, in the basement, and behind the dresser.		

10. Indicate whether the item contains complete sentences (Yes) or sentence fragments (No).

	Yes	No
Scientists have reported the discovery of a new exoplanet that orbits a star outside the solar system.	○	○
Named Ross 128b and considered a temperate planet.	○	○
Its temperate climate means that it is just warm enough for liquid water to exist on its surface.	○	○
Could Ross 128b sustain life? Scientists don't know yet.	○	○

Name: ______________________________ Date: ________________

Lesson 2: Command of Capitalization,Punctuation,and Spelling

1. Which homophone correctly completes the following sentence: "I wonder if ______ going to join us for dinner."

Ⓐ their
Ⓑ they're
Ⓒ there
Ⓓ thier

2. Which sentence uses a colon in the correct place?

Ⓐ Please bring these items to class: pencil, textbook, and calculator.
Ⓑ Please bring these items: to class pencil, textbook, and calculator.
Ⓒ Please: bring these items to class pencil, textbook, and calculator.
Ⓓ Please bring these items to class pencil textbook: and calculator.

3. Which is NOT a correct use of a colon? Write the answer in the box below.

Ⓐ To combine two dependent clauses.
Ⓑ To introduce a list.
Ⓒ To start a formal business letter.
Ⓓ To introduce a quote longer than three lines.

4. A semicolon should be placed AFTER which word in the following sentence: "Hope fully the rain will end soon otherwise we will have to cancel the football game."

Ⓐ Hopefully
Ⓑ soon
Ⓒ otherwise
Ⓓ cancel

Name: ______________________ Date: ______________

5. Which homophone correctly completes the following sentence: "Sometimes I feel ____ tired to get up in the morning."

Ⓐ to
Ⓑ two
Ⓒ toe
Ⓓ too

6. A comma should be placed AFTER which word in the following sentence: "Soon after moving to a new house Thomas and Denny made friends with their neighbors"?

Ⓐ Soon
Ⓑ moving
Ⓒ house
Ⓓ friends

7. Rewrite the following sentence correctly using a semicolon and a conjunctive adverb:

"Mark did not study for the final exam. He will probably not pass the test."

8. **John is writing an article for the school newspaper. He brings you his draft to be edited. Rewrite this part of the article, correcting four errors in capitalization.**

"East high School proudly presents the award winning musical Bye Bye Birdie. This Family-friendly show will run for one weekend only. filled with explosive tap dance numbers, Bye bye Birdie is a musical performance not to be missed!"

Name: ______________________ Date: ______________

9. Fill in the blank with the two correct punctuation marks needed to complete the sentence.

Instruction: Place the correct punctuation mark, leave one space and also write it in words (example: - dash)

	First Mark	Second Mark
Mary Kate screamed at the top of her lungs. __If I don't see that room cleaned by the end of the day__ there will be hell to pay!"		
James Joyce's Ulysses is considered one of the finest works of modernist fiction published__ however__ publication was made difficult for editors due to errors purposefully included by the author		
Father has brought several different kinds of vegetables from the store__ carrots, celery, and beets. Which would you prefer__		
Martin Luther King Jr.'s "Letter from Birmingham Jail" lists circumstances which African Americans have had to cope with. King writes, "When you have seen vicious mobs lynch your mothers and fathers at will and drown your sisters and brothers at whim__ when you have seen hate-filled policemen curse, kick, brutalize, and even kill your black brothers and sisters with impunity__" and so on, to foster empathy among readers.		

10. **Check Correct or Incorrect to indicate the correctly spelled word in the following table.**

	Correct	Incorrect
definitely	○	○
ocasionally	○	○
publically	○	○
accidentally	○	○

Lesson 3: Functions of Language

1. Select the author's name in this Works Cited entry for a book.

Foster, Thomas C. How to read literature like a professor: a lively and entertaining guide to reading between the lines. Harper, an imprint of HarperCollins Publishers, 2017.

Ⓐ Harper Collins
Ⓑ How to Read Literature Like a Professor
Ⓒ Thomas C. Foster
Ⓓ Foster C. Thomas

2. Select the title of the source in this Works Cited entry for an article.

Coscarelli, Joe. "Taylor Swift's 'Reputation' Sells 1.2 Million Copies in Its First Week." The NewYork Times, 21 Nov. 2017.

Ⓐ Joe Coscarelli
Ⓑ Taylor Swift
Ⓒ Reputation
Ⓓ The New York Times

3. Which is the only piece of information a reader CAN NOT learn from this Works Cited entry? Write the answer in the box below.

Shane, A. L. "Cell phones take parents' attention away from kids on playgrounds." Journal of the American Academy of Pediatrics, vol. 26, no. 1, Jan. 2011, pp. 5–15.

Ⓐ The length of the article in pages
Ⓑ The source of the article
Ⓒ The date the reader downloaded the article
Ⓓ The date the author published the article

4. Complete the analogy. Graceful is to awkward as excruciating is to

Ⓐ unbearable
Ⓑ mild
Ⓒ painful
Ⓓ excess

5. Complete the analogy. Gasoline is to tank as money is to

Ⓐ vault
Ⓑ silo
Ⓒ mattress
Ⓓ store

6. Complete the analogy. Obvious is to conspicuous as astonishing is to

Ⓐ boring
Ⓑ thrilling
Ⓒ desired
Ⓓ emotional

7. Tanya's Health teacher has assigned students to complete a report on the effects of chewing tobacco. The teacher has warned students to paraphrase the information they find during their research.

Explain the difference between plagiarizing and paraphrasing.

Name: ______________________ Date: ______________

8. Read the background information, then answer the question in an extended response. In 1830, President Andrew Jackson passed the Indian Removal Act. This law stated that Native Americans must move west of the Mississippi River and allow white settlers to take their land. U.S. soldiers were sent to remove the Native Americans by force and march them west. Many thousands of Native Americans died on this journey, 'which became known in history as "The Trail of Tears".

Explain how an encyclopedia article written about this historic event would differ from a first-hand account of the event written by one of the Native Americans who experienced the Trail of Tears. What is the purpose of each type of source (encyclopedia vs. first-hand account)?

9. Effective writers choose precise language to more accurately portray their meaning. Replace the word said in each sentence with a more precise verb that is specific to the intended meaning of each sentence. Choose the precise word from the word bank given. Word Bank: acknowledged, whispered, admitted, gasped, pondered, exclaimed, pleaded.

Common Verb	Precise Verb
"Shhh!" Melanie said. "Be quiet or you will wake up Mom and Dad.".	
"Touch down! The North High football team has just won the state championship!" said the announcer.	
"Can you please help me to clean up the classroom?" said the teacher.	

Name: ______________________ Date: ______________

10. For each phrase, indicate if the language represents formal academic language or informal social language.

	Formal	Informal
What's up, Jose? How you doin' today?.	○	○
I hear what you are saying, but I must respectfully disagree.	○	○
I am calling to inform you that I have scheduled your interview for next week.	○	○
Whoa, did you see the trick that kid did on his skateboard? He's got mad skills!	○	○

Name: ______________________ Date: ______________

Lesson 4: Determining Unknown Words

1. **Read the sentence. Based on the context, determine the meaning of the underlined word. "It was the Student Council president's job to disseminate information about the school events to the students in her class, making sure everyone was informed."**

Ⓐ spread
Ⓑ keep secret
Ⓒ disorganize
Ⓓ decide

2. **Read the sentence. Based on the context, determine the meaning of the underlined word. "In countries where the government is controlled by a dictator, officials usually jail dissidents who disagree with the laws."**

Ⓐ criminals
Ⓑ protesters
Ⓒ teachers
Ⓓ government officials

3. **Read the sentence. Based on the context, determine the meaning of the underlined word. "The teacher kept the class running smoothly by facilitating the lesson sequence, keeping everyone on task."**

Ⓐ controlling
Ⓑ reporting
Ⓒ organizing
Ⓓ cancelling

4. **Repeat, rename, and rebuild all begin with the prefix re-. What is the meaning of the prefix re-? Write the answer in the box below.**

Ⓐ not
Ⓑ before
Ⓒ again
Ⓓ under

5. Unfinished, unskilled, and unfriendly all begin with the prefix un-. What is the meaning of the prefix un-?

Ⓐ not
Ⓑ before
Ⓒ again
Ⓓ under

6. Childish, snobbish, and stylish all end with the suffix -ish. What is the meaning of the suffix -ish?

Ⓐ the act of
Ⓑ becoming
Ⓒ without
Ⓓ having the quality of

7. The root word bene means "good". What can you infer about a person who is described as being benevolent?

8. Denyae comes across an unfamiliar word while completing her homework. She decides to look it up in the dictionary. Besides reading the definition of the word, describe two other pieces of information a dictionary entry can provide to help her understand the word.

9. For each word, indicate the part of speech.

Word	Part of Speech
White House	
we	
disappear	
carefully	
and	
dirty	

10. Indicate whether the underlined word is acting as an adjective or an adverb in each sentence.

	Adjective	Adverb
It was a hot afternoon.	○	○
It was a terribly hot afternoon.	○	○
The afternoon sun was terribly hot.	○	○

Name: ______________________ Date: ______________

Lesson 5: Figurative Language

1. Which figure of speech is being used in the highlighted part of this text? "I'm so hungry I could eat a horse," Stan complained.

Ⓐ euphemism
Ⓑ hyperbole
Ⓒ alliteration
Ⓓ irony

2. Which figure of speech is being used in the underlined part of this text? "After her dog died, <u>a dark cloud hung over her head</u>, and she moped around in sorrow."

Ⓐ personification
Ⓑ hyperbole
Ⓒ simile
Ⓓ metaphor

3. Authors often use the phrase "forbidden fruit" to describe something tempting. This is a reference to the story of the Tree of Knowledge in the Bible, the sacred text for those of the Christian faith. This figure of speech is also known as?

Ⓐ alliteration
Ⓑ assonance
Ⓒ allusion
Ⓓ illusion

4. Which figure of speech is being used in the highlighted part of this text? "The pep per tickled her nose, causing her to sneeze right into her dish."

Ⓐ personification
Ⓑ hyperbole
Ⓒ simile
Ⓓ metaphor

Name: ______________________ Date: ______________

5. When a person dies, they are often said to have "passed away". This substitution for a gentler phrase is known as...

Ⓐ personification
Ⓑ euphemism
Ⓒ metaphor
Ⓓ hyperbole

6. Phrases such as "jumbo shrimp", "minor crisis", and "awfully good" are examples of what figure of speech?

Ⓐ oxymoron
Ⓑ hyperbole
Ⓒ simile
Ⓓ metaphor

7. The denotation of "house" and "home" are similar. Explain how the connotation of "house"and "home" differ.

Name: ______________________ Date: ______________

8. The denotation of "slender" and "gaunt" are similar, but their connotations differ. Explain how the context of the sentence effects when an author would use "slender" versus "gaunt".

9. Read the excerpt from the poem "The Bells" by Edgar Allan Poe. Complete the table with another example of alliteration from this excerpt (some answers have been provided). Include only the word pairs that demonstrate the technique.

"Hear the sledges with the bells—

Silver bells!

What a world of merriment their melody foretells!"

Alliteration	

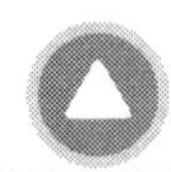

10. Read the excerpts from the poem "The Raven" by Edgar Allan Poe. Check Yes or No to indicate whether the line contains assonance or not.

	Yes	No
"Once upon a midnight dreary"	◯	◯
"For the rare and radiant maiden whom the angels name Lenore."	◯	◯
"And the silken, sad, uncertain rustling of each purple curtain"	◯	◯

Name: ______________________ Date: ______________

Lesson 6: Academic and Domain-Specific Vocabulary

1. Choose the academic term that best completes the sentence. "China's _______ is largely dependent on manufacturing with 80% of their exports being manufactured goods."

Ⓐ government
Ⓑ research
Ⓒ bank
Ⓓ economy

2. Choose the academic term that best completes the sentence. "The main task of the ____ branch of the United States government is to make laws."

Ⓐ executive
Ⓑ legislative
Ⓒ congressional
Ⓓ judicial

3. Choose the academic term that best completes the sentence. "Clare conducted an ____ of the way children learn to read as the subject of her Master's thesis to complete her second college degree."

Ⓐ analysis
Ⓑ research
Ⓒ data
Ⓓ summary

4. Choose the academic term that best completes the sentence. "For teenagers, whose brains are not yet fully developed, the ____ of rational and irrational thinking is not always clear."

Ⓐ principles
Ⓑ concepts
Ⓒ roles
Ⓓ factors

5. Choose the academic term that best completes the sentence. "The police had to free the suspected burglar because there was not enough ___ to convict him."

Ⓐ legal
Ⓑ theory
Ⓒ evidence
Ⓓ witness

6. Choose the academic term that best completes the sentence. "I can ____ from the clothes and hairstyles in this photograph that it was taken during the 1980s."

Ⓐ infer
Ⓑ analyze
Ⓒ evaluate
Ⓓ summarize

7. Read the quote spoken by former President Barack Obama. Paraphrase the quote in your own words.

"Change will not come if we wait for some other time. We are the ones we've been waiting for. We are the change we seek."

Name: ______________________________ Date: ________________

8. Read the passage. Summarize the central idea of the passage.

"Sustainability is the hot buzzword among scientists and environmentalists right now. But what, exactly, does it mean? Sustainability is the capacity of the earth's natural systems to adapt and survive in changing environmental conditions. Earth has an extraordinary ability to maintain a healthy balance in its temperature, energy, and food chains. Although humans have only existed on earth for a fraction of the planet's existence, there is increasing evidence that humans have seriously affected earth's ecosystems in ways that may compromise its ability to sustain itself. For example, humans are using renewable resources, like trees, faster than the earth can replace them. If humans do not adopt sustainable practices, the damage may be irreversible. Sustainable practices ensure that businesses and individuals consume fewer resources and in a way that does not damage the earth's ecosystems."

9. Choose the correct academic word to complete the sentence. Type the correct answer in the second column.

Sentence	Correct Word
The scientists uncovered a bone that was (approximately/appropriately) one foot long.	
Sean's greatest (arbitrary/attribute) is his ability to always see the good in everyone.	
The starting gun signaled that the track race was about to (commence/compensate).	
Nicole planned to (compile/comprehensive) all of her data into a report for her boss.	

10. For each statement, indicate if the underlined academic word is used correctly.

	Correct	Incorrect
Despite his strong feelings about the case, the judge had to remain objective and fair when hearing both sides of the argument.	◯	◯
The gardener showed his ambiguity towards his work when he cut corners and put forth little effort.	◯	◯
Zeus, Hera, and Poseidon are some of the main characters in Greek mythology.	◯	◯
The first chapters of a book usually includes expository information to fill in the reader on essential background knowledge.	◯	◯

Name: ________________________ Date: ______________

Writing Standards

Lesson 1: Writing Arguments To Support Claims

1. The most important sentence(s) in your argument is ________.Write your answer in the box given below .

2. What are the five steps in the writing process that you should use to prepare your argument?

Name: ______________________ Date: ______________

3. Which of the following is part of the perfect paragraph?

Ⓐ Topic Sentence
Ⓑ Supporting Sentences
Ⓒ Clincher
Ⓓ All of the above
Ⓔ None of the above

4. In a traditional 5 paragraph argument essay, how many points should you discuss in your thesis?

Ⓐ One
Ⓑ Seven
Ⓒ Three
Ⓓ Two

5. Which paragraph includes the thesis in a 5 paragraph essay?

Ⓐ Supporting Paragraph #1
Ⓑ Conclusion
Ⓒ Introduction
Ⓓ None of the above

6. What is a topic sentence?

Ⓐ A sentence that has to link back to your thesis.
Ⓑ The first sentence of a paragraph.
Ⓒ A sentence that tells what your paragraph will be about.
Ⓓ All of the above.

7. Which sentence makes the best thesis statement?

Ⓐ Even though McDonalds seems to be the food of choice for children, families are rejecting the pressure to feed children there and choosing better qualities of food.
Ⓑ I am going to explain why children should eat better food than McDonalds.
Ⓒ McDonalds is bad.
Ⓓ None of the above.

Name: ______________________ Date: ______________

8. These words are very important in an argument because they allow you to move between ideas helping you to connect, compare, and contrast your sentences and paragraphs:

Ⓐ transitions
Ⓑ connectives
Ⓒ metaphors
Ⓓ paragraphs

9. Determine whether the following statement is True or False.

In an argument, opinions must be proven with facts, expert testimonies, and other evidence to be considered valid.

Ⓐ True
Ⓑ False

10. In your argument's conclusion, you should:

Ⓐ Restate your thesis.
Ⓑ Remind the reader of how you supported the thesis.
Ⓒ Make a final impression on the reader to emphasize the importance of the essay.
Ⓓ All of the above.

Lesson 2: Writing Informative/Explanatory Texts

1. When you are writing to inform or explain you should:

Ⓐ List a lot of really good facts
Ⓑ Use a lot of opinions
Ⓒ Write in first person
Ⓓ None of the above

2. Which of the following is the MOST important part of informing or explaining?

Ⓐ Opinions
Ⓑ Facts
Ⓒ Hyperbole
Ⓓ None of the above

3. Which of the following pieces of writing is MOST likely to be informative?

Ⓐ A set of directions to the mall.
Ⓑ An explanation of how to knit.
Ⓒ An explanation of the causes of WWI.
Ⓓ All of the above.

4. When you organize your writing for an informational text, you should use

Ⓐ Big paragraphs
Ⓑ Bullet point lists
Ⓒ Complex sentences
Ⓓ None of the above

5. True or false, this is a sentence you would see in an informational text. Write your answer in the box given below.

Get down to Marty's Auto Shop and get this amazing deal on tires today!

6. Determine if the following statement is true or false, then explain your reasoning in the box below.

The Amazon Rain Forest has many different types of lizards in it; some of the rarest creatures in the world.

7. You would be most likely to see the following in an informational text:

Ⓐ Maps
Ⓑ Diagrams
Ⓒ Lists
Ⓓ All of the above

8. This type of informative writing tends to use steps. For example: If you want to bake a pie, first you need a decent pie crust. Then you fill the crust with whatever you want cherries, blueberries, etc. Finally you put another layer of crust on top. Then bake.

Ⓐ Descriptive
Ⓑ Order and sequence
Ⓒ Problem and solution
Ⓓ Cause and effect
Ⓔ None of the above

9. In order and sequence writing, the most important supporting words you will use are:

Ⓐ Transitions
Ⓑ Conjunctions
Ⓒ Adjectives
Ⓓ Adverbs

Name: ______________________ Date: ______________

10. A good strategy after researching your topic, is to organize your information in:

Ⓐ An outline
Ⓑ A mental map
Ⓒ Diagram
Ⓓ All of the above

Name: ______________________ Date: ______________

Lesson 3: Write Narratives

1. Write the word that matches the definition in column A

A	B
Series of events in a story	
The source of tension in the story	
The beginning of a story when the characters and setting are introduced	

2. When you write an exposition, which story elements should you include?

3. Select the definition that matches the first column.

	After the climax and before the resolution	Before the climax and after the exposition	The moment of greatest intensity in the story
Rising action	○	○	○
Falling action	○	○	○
Climax	○	○	○

4. Which type of narrator uses "I" to tell their story?

Ⓐ Second person
Ⓑ Third person limited
Ⓒ First person
Ⓓ Third person omniscient

5. In non-fiction, which type of character tends to grow and learn from the conflict?

Ⓐ Flat
Ⓑ Static
Ⓒ Dynamic
Ⓓ Antagonist

6. When you want a character to speak in a story, which type of punctuation to let the reader know that a character is speaking?

Ⓐ Periods
Ⓑ Quotation marks
Ⓒ Exclamation marks
Ⓓ Question marks

7. When you spend time describing the time and place the story takes place, this is called ?

Ⓐ Setting
Ⓑ Plot
Ⓒ Dialogue
Ⓓ Conflict

8. The correct order for a traditional story is

Ⓐ Exposition, rising action, climax, falling action, and resolution
Ⓑ Rising action, exposition, falling action, climax, and resolution
Ⓒ Exposition, rising action, resolution, climax, and falling action
Ⓓ Climax, rising action, falling action, climax, resolution

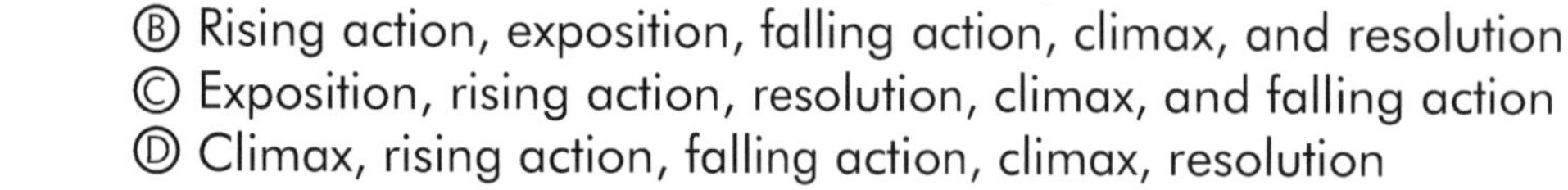

Name: ______________________ Date: ______________

9. The event in the plot that kicks off the rising action is called:

Ⓐ Trigger incident
Ⓑ Inciting incident
Ⓒ Climax
Ⓓ None of the above

10. In the below plot chart, which event is c:

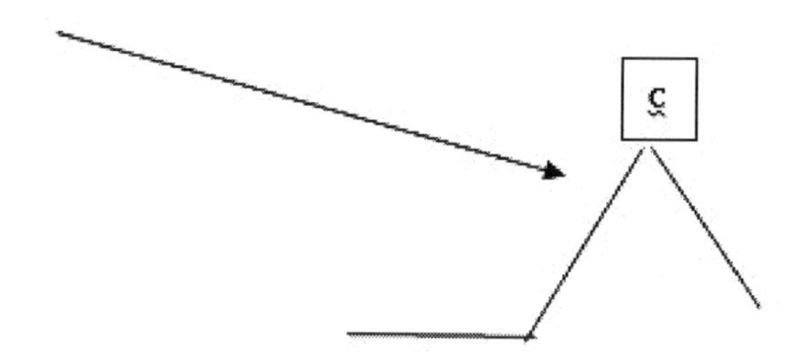

Ⓐ Rising Action
Ⓑ Climax
Ⓒ Exposition
Ⓓ Falling Action

Name: ______________________ Date: ______________

Lesson 4: Produce Clear and Coherent Writing

1. Select the writing type that matches the definition in the table below.

	Persuasive writing	Informational writing	Narrative writing
Writing that uses bullet points, graphs, and images to tell the reader about a particular topic	○	○	○
Writing that is designed to convince the reader of the writer's point	○	○	○
A style of writing that includes plot and character	○	○	○

2. Which type of writing uses hyperbole to emphasize a point?

3. If you wanted to produce a piece of informational writing, what characteristics would be there?

Name: ______________________ Date: ______________

4. Choose from the following list and determine which type of writing would match the example in column A

Informational	Narrative	Persuasive	Descriptive

A	B
A letter from a child to his mother explaining why King Charles Cavalier is the best.	
A pamphlet about the different types of cocker spaniels.	
A fictional story about a dog named George and his owner Evie.	

5. Which type of writing uses sensory details and metaphors? Write your answer in the box below

Ⓐ Narrative
Ⓑ Exposition
Ⓒ Persuasive
Ⓓ Informative

6. You are absolutely disgusted with how your town handles waste, and you want some thing done about it. Which type of writing would you use?

Ⓐ Narrative
Ⓑ Exposition
Ⓒ Persuasive
Ⓓ Informative

7. What type of writing is this?

Costa Rica is a wonderful place to visit, and you should come here too. The amazing green and blue of the country invites you in to really feel enveloped in the luxury of the country.

Ⓐ Narrative
Ⓑ Exposition
Ⓒ Persuasive
Ⓓ Informative

8. Which of the following are considered informational texts?

Ⓐ Sequence
Ⓑ Problem and Solution
Ⓒ Cause and Effect
Ⓓ All of the above

9. What is the topic of this piece of writing?

When we think about the minimum age for voting, the first question that comes to our mind is: How young is too young? The minimum ages vary in the different context such as that for driving, marriage, joining the army and so on. While there is an argument that 16 and 17 year-olds are too immature to vote, there is also a danger that they might not vote at all.

Ⓐ Young people
Ⓑ Voting importance for young people
Ⓒ Immaturity of 16 year olds
Ⓓ Adults not trusting teenagers

10. What is the purpose of this piece of writing?

When we think about the minimum age for voting, the first question that comes to our mind is: How young is too young? The minimum ages vary in the different context such as that for driving, marriage, joining the army and so on. While there is an argument that 16 and 17-year-olds are too immature to vote, there is also a danger that they might not vote at all.

Ⓐ The purpose is to inform the reader of voting history in America.
Ⓑ The purpose is to persuade the reader to review the importance of voting with our teenagers.
Ⓒ The purpose is to describe voting habits of American teens.
Ⓓ The purpose is to persuade the reader about why teenagers should have more responsibility.

Name: ______________________ Date: ______________

Lesson 5: Develop and Strengthen Writing

1. Arrange the terms following the correct order of the writing process and place your answers in the boxes given below.

Ⓐ Drafting
Ⓑ Revising
Ⓒ Proofreading
Ⓓ Planning
Ⓔ Publishing

2. Why is it important to know the writing process to create a polished piece of work? Explain your answer.

3. Which state of the writing process tends to be the most complex and requires the most amount of time?

4. If you are in the revising stage, you should focus on punctuation and capitalization.

Ⓐ True
Ⓑ False

5. Which of the following sentences shows evidence of having been proof read correctly:

Ⓐ When we think about the minimum age for voting, the first question that comes to our mind is: How young is too young.
Ⓑ When we think about the minimum age for voting, the first question that comes to our mind is; How young is too young!
Ⓒ When we think about the minimum age for voting, the first question that comes to our mind is: How young is too young?
Ⓓ When we think about the minimum age for voting. The first question that comes to our mind is: How young is too young?

6. Which of the following are acceptable in the pre-writing stage?

Ⓐ Mental map
Ⓑ Outline
Ⓒ Free write
Ⓓ All of the above

7. How would you correct the following sentence?

The new exhibit at the Museum of Modern Art in New York City is really amazing

Ⓐ All the words should be lower case
Ⓑ You need a comma after exhibit
Ⓒ Modern Art should be lower case
Ⓓ None of the above

8. Which of the following sentences has a dependent clause?

Ⓐ Let's go skiing tomorrow.
Ⓑ When did George get a tic?
Ⓒ Because I love dogs, I want four when I am older.
Ⓓ I want 10 presents for Christmas and I will give 10 presents to a charity.

9. Determine whether the following statement is True or False.

	True	False
Informal writing is okay in the proofreading stage of writing	◯	◯

10. When you write you should vary between complex, compound and simple sentences because this will keep your writing:

Ⓐ Challenging to others to read
Ⓑ Varied and interesting
Ⓒ Sounding smart
Ⓓ Humorous

Name: ______________________ Date: ______________

Lesson 6:Use Technology to Produce,Publish, and Update Writing Products

1. If you copy information from the Internet and use it in your writing without citing it as a source, you are:

Ⓐ Creating
Ⓑ Adjusting
Ⓒ Plagiarizing
Ⓓ None of the above

2. What is it called when you let the reader know where your source came from?

Ⓐ Citing Sources
Ⓑ Repeating sources
Ⓒ Doctoring sources
Ⓓ Bibiliographing sources

3. What is paraphrasing and do you need to cite it?

4. What should be the following characteristics of a good research topic?

Ⓐ focused on a few variables
Ⓑ can be researched and proven with evidence
Ⓒ the topic should be substantial
Ⓓ all of the above

Name: ______________________ Date: ______________

5. Which of the following are styles you can use to cite and reference your paper? Write your answer in the box given below.

Ⓐ MLA
Ⓑ APA
Ⓒ Chicago
Ⓓ All of the above

6. Where would you place a citation like this in your research paper:

Havard, Frances. "Teacher on a Mission: Saving Students from Plagiairism." The New York Times, 22 May 2017, www.francestimes.com/2017/05/22/teachers.html?_r=0. Accessed 17 May 2018.

Ⓐ Works Cited page
Ⓑ Introduction
Ⓒ Right after you use a quote from the article in the body of your essay
Ⓓ In the conclusion

7. How should you offset a direct quote that is less than four lines from a source in your writing?

Ⓐ Use a colon to indicate a quote is beginning
Ⓑ Put the quote within quotation marks
Ⓒ Put the quote in italics
Ⓓ Underline the quote

8. Websites ending in _____ are the best to use when citing your sources

Ⓐ .com
Ⓑ .edu
Ⓒ .org
Ⓓ b and c only

9. Determine whether the following statement is True or False.

	True	False
Wikipedia is a reliable source to use in your writing		

Name: ______________________ Date: ______________

10. How should you organize your research?

Ⓐ Index cards
Ⓑ OneNote
Ⓒ Google Forms
Ⓓ All of the above

Name: ______________________ Date: ______________

Lesson 7:Conduct Short and Sustained research Project

1. Determine whether the following statement is True or False.

There is no need for print sources, and it is appropriate only to use the Internet in your research.

Ⓐ True
Ⓑ False

2. True or False. The following would be considered a good research topic.

How do cigarettes affect 16-18 year old boys physically?	

3. Based on the prompt "Prepare a report about something you are interested in," what is the process for selecting a good research topic?

Ⓐ Identify 2 or 3 interests and prepare your index cards for researching those topics.
Ⓑ Identify 2 or 3 interests, and determine which is researchable and most interesting to you, and then formulate a question about that interest.
Ⓒ Tell the teacher that you have no interests and don't know what to write about.
Ⓓ Start writing about what you like and research after.

4. Why would this research question need to be revised: How do we damage our environment?

5. In a two-page research project, what is an appropriate number of sources to cite?

Ⓐ 6
Ⓑ 3
Ⓒ 9
Ⓓ 1

Name: ______________________ Date: ______________

6. Why is it important to create a research question as one of the first steps in the writing process?

Ⓐ It helps narrow down what is being researched and lays the groundwork for what will be researched.
Ⓑ It helps the researcher to group and categorize different aspects of their thesis.
Ⓒ It sets up the structure of the paper.
Ⓓ It helps you gather the quotes for your essay.

7. Arrange the following terms of the research process in their correct order.

Ⓐ Proofread
Ⓑ Publish
Ⓒ Brainstorm topics
Ⓓ Group/Organize research making connections
Ⓔ Draft
Ⓕ Revise
Ⓖ Research, choosing applicable sources
Ⓗ Craft a research question

Name: ______________________ Date: ______________

8. After you select a topic, what is the next step in the research process?

9. Which of the following sources does NOT need to be included in your bibliography or works cited page?

Ⓐ Title of a magazine
Ⓑ Author's Name
Ⓒ Publishing House
Ⓓ None of the above

10. Determine whether the following statement is True or False.

	True	False
When searching for information on your topic, you should focus exclusively on .org, .edu, and .gov sites so your source is more credible.	○	○

Lesson 8:Source-Based Writing

1. An Earth Science teacher wants to take his students on a field trip to the local science museum. Which source is likely to be the most useful in planning this field trip?

Ⓐ A review from a local blogger describing her experience at the science museum with her two young children.
Ⓑ The city's tourist information website listing local attractions.
Ⓒ A list of all the places the school has taken students for field trips previously.
Ⓓ The science museum's official website.

2. Which is the correct way to order a Works Cited page in MLA format?

Ⓐ Alphabetized by author's last name.
Ⓑ In the order that the sources are cited in the paper.
Ⓒ In the order that the writer found and read each source.
Ⓓ By the date of the source was published, from oldest to most recent.

3. A movie critic is writing a review on James Cameron's 1997 film Titanic. He is attempting to convince his audience that the movie is of high quality. Which of the following pieces of evidence is biased?

Ⓐ Leonardo DiCaprio's performance steals the show
Ⓑ The movie was nominated for 14 academy awards
Ⓒ Initially the movie grossed over $1.8 billion
Ⓓ The movie is based on true events

4. A student is researching the opioid epidemic in America in an attempt to bring awareness to his classmates. He hopes to provide detailed information on how the drug problem affects Americans. Which of the following sources of information is likely to be the most credible?

Ⓐ an interview with the school nurse about the risk factors for students
Ⓑ statistics of drug-related deaths from the US Department of Health and Human Services
Ⓒ information about psychological effects of drugs found on an online forum
Ⓓ a drug counselling brochure provided by a local pharmacy

5. An essayist is attempting to write a review of Alice Walker's short story "Flowers." In the essay, the essayist claims that Walker uses flowers as a symbol to represent the main character's innocence. Which of the following pieces of evidence is not relevant to the claim?

Ⓐ "At the end of the story, Myop lays down her flowers at the dead man's body to signify her new understanding of racially motivated killings"
Ⓑ "Myop starts the story gathering flowers that are blooming during the fall harvest. During her initial gathering she hums a tune and plays around the farm with a childlike attitude."
Ⓒ "It isn't until Myop plucks the one wild rose she finds that she sees remnants of a noose and realizes the man had been lynched."
Ⓓ "Myop lays down her flowers at the man's feet as a way to memorialize him as if she had been gathering the flowers all along for that purpose."

6. What is the correct way to cite a source within a paper when the source has no author listed?

Ⓐ Use "Anonymous" in place of the author's name.
Ⓑ Use the title of the source in place of the author's name.
Ⓒ Use your own name in place of the author's name.
Ⓓ Leave out the author's name and use the page number by itself.

7. Read the passage from the original source, then read the student's text used in an academic paper. Answer the question using evidence from the texts.

Source Text: Stokely Carmichael was born in Port of Spain, Trinidad and Tobago, on June 29, 1941. Carmichael rose to prominence as a member and later the chairman of SNCC, the Student Nonviolent Coordinating Committee, working with Martin Luther King Jr. and other Southern leaders to stage protests. Carmichael later lost faith in the tactic of nonviolence, promoting "Black Power" and allying himself with the militant Black Panther Party. -Published by Biography.com

Student Text: Stokely Carmichael was an influential leader in the Civil Rights Movement. Although at first he worked alongside major leaders like Martin Luther King Jr. to promote the cause of racial equality with nonviolent protests, he later made a radical change. Frustrated by the lack of progress, he became a militant protester, popularizing the phrase "Black Power" to represent this new view of activism.

Is the student's text plagiarized? Explain why or why not.

8. Maria is writing a report on the causes of the Civil War for Social Studies class. She is planning to use the phrase "American wars" as her keyterm in the search engine. Explain why this is not the most effective search term for her to use in her research. Suggest a strong search term that will yield better results.

Name: ______________________ Date: ______________

9. Choose the correct word to complete the sentence based on the context. Type the correct answer in the second column.

Sentence	Correct word
Of all the information, quotes, and data points that could be used in an academic paper, an effective writer must (assess/accurately) which should be used based on the research question.	
(Assessment/Authoritative) sources are those that are connected to well known and respected publishers, universities, newspapers, journals, and authors.	
To ensure that the paper is balanced and unbiased, an effective writer must be cautious of (overreliance/paraphrasing) on just one source.	
An effective writer must have a clear, focused research question in order to find the most (relevant/relatable) information that addresses the topic of study.	

Name: ______________________ Date: ______________

10. Read each bibliographic citation. Check Correct or Incorrect to indicate if it is written in the correct MLA format.

	Correct	Incorrect
Smith stated that the habit of slouching over a computer will have long-term effects on one's posture and spinal health. (263).	○	○
No other musician "has had as much influence on the music industry" (Johnston 322).	○	○
Harriet Gladwell explains that in those days, women were unable to own property, enter into contracts, or earn a salary (Gladwell, "Women and Power").	○	○

Name: ______________________ Date: ______________

Lesson 9:Citing Text -Evidence

1. Read the passage and answer the questions.

Teenagers often board school buses before most people have even gotten out of bed, causing chronic sleep deprivation, a major public health concern. This should be scary enough to debate national reform to school schedules. Now researchers that starting school later in the morning, no earlier than 8:30 am, would actually have financial benefits as well. Students who are better rested perform better in school; this translates to better career opportunities later in life which has a positive effect on the national economy. Also, fewer car crashes would result from drowsy teen-agers driving to school before they are fully awake.

What type of writing is the above passage?

Ⓐ narrative
Ⓑ informational
Ⓒ argument
Ⓓ Could be both B and C.

2. Which is the central idea of the above passage?

Ⓐ School buses pick up students too early in the morning.
Ⓑ Chronic sleep deprivation is a major public health concern.
Ⓒ Better rested students would result in better academic performance.
Ⓓ Implementing later school start times would have a positive health and economic effect.

Merry Autumn- by Paul Laurence Dunbar

Now purple tints are all around;
The sky is blue and mellow;
And e'en the grasses turn the ground
From modest green to yellow...

A butterfly goes winging by;
A singing bird comes after;
And Nature, all from earth to sky,
Is bubbling o'er with laughter...

The earth is just so full of fun
It really can't contain it;
And streams of mirth so freely run
The heavens seem to rain it...

Why, it's the climax of the year,—
The highest time of living!—
Till naturally its bursting cheer
Just melts into thanksgiving.

3. Read the excerpt from the poem "Merry Autumn" by Paul Laurence Dunbar, then answer the question. Write the correct answer in the box given below.

The phrases "purple tints", "modest green", "singing bird", "bubbling o'er with laughter" are examples of...

Ⓐ personification.
Ⓑ sensory details.
Ⓒ metaphors.
Ⓓ onomatopoeia.

4. Read the excerpt from the poem "Merry Autumn" by Paul Laurence Dunbar, then answer the question.

Which line from the poem best captures the author's main idea?

Ⓐ "Now purple tints are all around"
Ⓑ "And Nature, all from earth to sky/Is bubbling o'er with laughter"
Ⓒ "Why, it's the climax of the year/The highest time of living" (Correct Answer)
Ⓓ "Till naturally its busting cheer/Just melts into thanksgiving"

5. Read the excerpt from My Antonia by Willa Cather, then answer the question.

"I had a sense of coming home to myself, and of having found out what a little circle man's experience is. For Ántonia and for me, this had been the road of Destiny; had taken us to those early accidents of fortune which predetermined for us all that we can ever be. Now I understood that the same road was to bring us together again. Whatever we had missed, we possessed together the precious, the incommunicable past." What is the meaning of the word "predetermined" as it is used in this context?

Ⓐ an accident or unfortunate circumstance
Ⓑ to be decided in advance
Ⓒ easy to agree upon
Ⓓ something that is flexible or unsettled

Name: ______________________ Date: ______________

6. Read the excerpt from My Antonia by Willa Cather, then answer the question.

"I had a sense of coming home to myself, and of having found out what a little circle man's experience is. For Ántonia and for me, this had been the road of Destiny; had taken us to those early accidents of fortune which predetermined for us all that we can ever be. Now I understood that the same road was to bring us together again. Whatever we had missed, we possessed together the precious, the incommunicable past."

Which statement best reflects the theme of this passage?

Ⓐ A person can not escape his/her past; it is always a part of you.
Ⓑ Nature is often a reflection of what a person is feeling inside.
Ⓒ Humans must overcome countless obstacles to realize the true meaning of life.
Ⓓ It is natural to fear "the other", or those who are different from yourself.

7. Read the excerpt from Little Women by Louisa May Alcott. Answer the short response question based on the text.

"Now, the garden separated the Marches' house from that of Mr. Laurence. Both stood in a suburb of the city, which was still country like, with groves and lawns, large gardens, and quiet streets. A low hedge parted the two estates. On one side was an old, brown house, looking rather bare and shabby, robbed of the vines that in summer covered its walls and the flowers, which then surrounded it. On the other side was a stately stone mansion, plainly betokening every sort of comfort and luxury, from the big coach house and well-kept grounds to the conservatory and the glimpses of lovely things one caught between the rich curtains."

How do the two houses described in the passage differ? Cite evidence from the text support your answer.

8. Troy is writing an essay about the health benefits of pets. Read his draft; then answer the question in an extended response.

"There are many reasons to love your dog. Now a new study has found another one; apparently, owning a dog reduces the risk of heart attack and other fatal conditions. Research shows that for people who live alone, their risk of cardiovascular disease is lessened by 36%. Scientists believe that this may be because dog owners are likely to be more active. Taking their dogs out for brisk walks and playing in the part encourages dog owners to exercise more which results in more exercise and stronger heart muscles . The study also proved that having a dog can reduce a child's risk of asthma. A dog's fur contains tiny microbes; being exposed to more bacteria can force a child's immune system to develop a stronger defense against disease. More significantly, dogs offer emotional support. Sure, they may chew your slippers and bark at the neighbors, but the benefits of dog ownership may just save your life!"

Troy wants to know if he has sufficient evidence to support his claim. Write a response that explains where he needs to develop his argument further, and why.

Name: ______________________ Date: ______________

9. Read the following infographic, then answer the question.

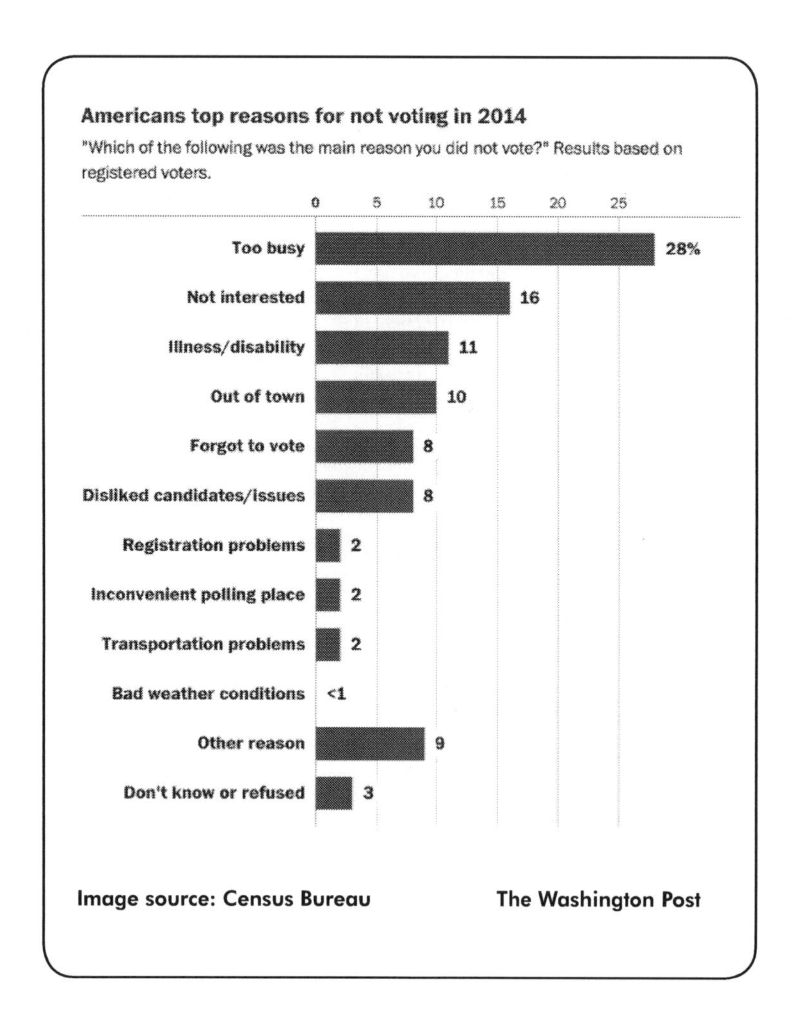

Based on the data in the infographic, rank the reasons Americans gave for not voting from the most common (1) to the least common response (5).

reasons for not voting	rank
Out of town	
Not interested	
Bad weather conditions	
Forgot to vote	
Too busy	

10. Read the political cartoon published in 1940 during World War II, then fill in the table.

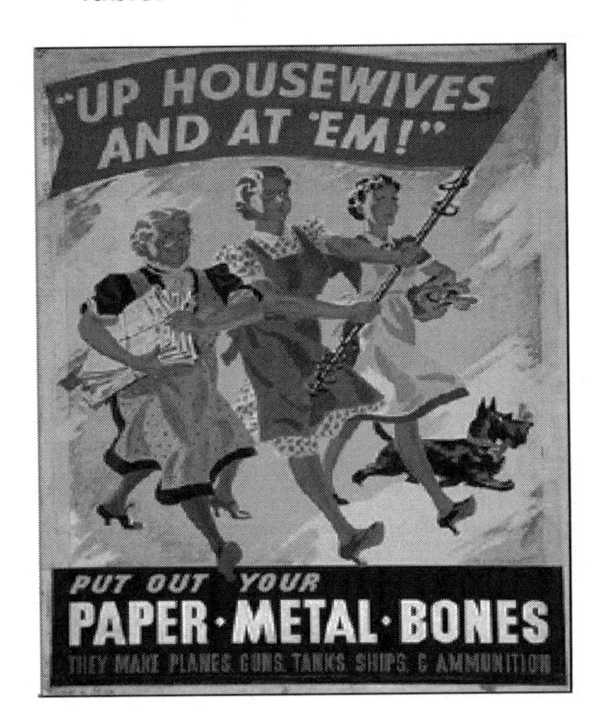

	Supported by Cartoon	Not Supported by Cartoon
Women were an important part of the war effort.	◯	◯
Dogs were an important part of the war effort.	◯	◯
Common home goods could be re-cycled into items needed by the mili-tary.	◯	◯
Americans should be suspicious of Japanese, Russians, and Italians	◯	◯

ADDITIONAL PRACTICE QUESTIONS

1. When a piece of literature is reset in a different time and place, this is called a(n):

Ⓐ Transformation
Ⓑ Adaptation
Ⓒ Sequel
Ⓓ Drama

2. Would a movie version of a book be considered an adaptation?

Ⓐ Yes
Ⓑ No

3. As a reader, how can you tell if something has been adapted from another text?

Ⓐ The characters names might be similar.
Ⓑ Key quotes from the original might appear in the adaptation.
Ⓒ The theme can be the same.
Ⓓ All of the above.

4. Determine whether the following statement is True or False.

Musical versions of a novel would NOT be considered an adaptation.

Ⓐ True
Ⓑ False

5. What would a reader gain from reading, watching, or listening to an adaptation of an original work?

Ⓐ They might gain insight into a character that they might not see in the original setting, making it easier to understand the character's traits in both genres.
Ⓑ It might deepen their understanding of a theme in the original work, when they see it in an other setting.
Ⓒ Both a and b
Ⓓ None of the above

6. When reading an article, after summarizing it, the reader should always identify next:

Ⓐ Words that use a strong connotation.
Ⓑ The thesis or the main purpose of the author's work.
Ⓒ The conclusion.
Ⓓ Supporting evidence.

7. Which of the following would most be considered analysis?

Ⓐ Summarizing the text.
Ⓑ Listing the main characters.
Ⓒ Identifying the different parts of the essay – introduction, conclusion, etc.
Ⓓ Exploring how the writer supports the argument by identifying key pieces of evidence.

8. When a writer introduces a piece of evidence, he/she should always:

Ⓐ Explain how that evidence links to that point.
Ⓑ Cite where the evidence comes from.
Ⓒ Link the evidence back to the larger thesis.
Ⓓ All of above.

9. Above all, literature can be a guide for humans to help guide us to live better lives. It is through the struggles of the protagonist that we learn about our own failings and show to grow. The obstacles characters face tend to strengthen the character, which is of course tied to the theme of the book. For example, in Great Expectations by Charles Dickens, the main character Pip has a very difficult childhood. His parents both die and his minder is an abusive older sister named, named Mrs. Joe Garger. By the end of the book, Pip learns to be a man and overcome these many struggles that he faces. This is true of any person, which is the point of literature, to reflect out reality. We like Pip, must learn to jump over the hurdles that are in our path and become stronger and better people. (written by Frances Havard)

In this article, the writer uses the example of Pip to illustrate which point?

Ⓐ Literature reflects reality.
Ⓑ We, like Pip, must overcome obstacles to become stronger people.
Ⓒ Literature can be used as a guide for living.
Ⓓ Pip is a character that gets stronger throughout the book.

10. Above all, literature can be a guide for humans to help guide us to live better lives. It is through the struggles of the protagonist that we learn about our own failings and show to grow. The obstacles characters face tend to strengthen the character, which is of course tied to the theme of the book. For example, in Great Expectations by Charles Dickens, the main character Pip has a very difficult childhood. His parents both die and his minder is an abusive older sister named, named Mrs. Joe Garger. By the end of the book, Pip learns to be a man and overcome these many struggles that he faces. This is true of any person, which is the point of literature, to reflect out reality. We like Pip, must learn to jump over the hurdles that are in our path and become stronger and better people. (written by Frances Havard)

One thing the author could have done to strengthen her argument would have been:

Ⓐ Pull a quote from the novel to show Pip's growth.
Ⓑ Spend more time talking about herself.
Ⓒ Describe more of Pip's challenges.
Ⓓ All of the above.
Ⓔ A and c only.

11. Which of the following is the most true about how a writer must develop his/her points?

Ⓐ They should always have a topic sentence and then supporting details
Ⓑ They should always have paragraphs
Ⓒ They should always have a conclusion
Ⓓ They should always have a hook at the opening of the essay
Ⓔ None of the above

Name: ______________________ Date: ______________

12. In an essay, the most important sentence is:

Ⓐ The thesis
Ⓑ The first topic sentence in paragraph 2
Ⓒ The last line of the conclusion
Ⓓ The one with the most words

13. How can studying multimedia help you develop skills?

Ⓐ It develops critical thinking skills.
Ⓑ It helps you understand how bias is used to present a subject matter.
Ⓒ It helps you understand how different types of media shape our impressions of a subject.
Ⓓ All of the above.

14.

A

The Washington Times

SUNDAY EVENING EDITION

WAR DECLARED; ALL EUROPE IN TURMOIL

AUSTRIAN TROOPS ARE MOVING ON BELGRADE, EVACUATED BY SERBS

Kingdom Stake and King Pawn in War

B

What type of multimedia source is A?

Ⓐ Essay
Ⓑ Newspaper
Ⓒ Website
Ⓓ Video

15. Which multimedia source does a better job of showing the fact that all of Europe is at war? Why?

Name: ______________________________ Date: ______________

16.

The New York Times.

HEIR TO AUSTRIA'S THRONE IS SLAIN WITH HIS WIFE BY A BOSNIAN YOUTH TO AVENGE SEIZURE OF HIS COUNTRY

Francis Ferdinand Shot During State Visit to Sarajevo.

TWO ATTACKS IN A DAY

Slain by Assassin's Bullets.

In the above newspaper print, how can the audience tell that the newspaper writers sympathize with Austria?

Ⓐ The headline uses the words "slain" which suggest murder and makes the archduke a victim.
Ⓑ The pictures present the archduke and his wife as innocent.
Ⓒ The reference to an "assassin" indicates the crime andputs the archduke and his wife in the role of victim.
Ⓓ All of the above.

17. Multimedia messages are built to impact the reader emotionally and to enhance their perspective on the subject matter.

Ⓐ True
Ⓑ False

Name: ______________________ Date: ______________

18. When a multimedia presentation is written, the chief concern of a writer's attention is to whom?

19.

In the above advertisement for Jell-O, which phrase uses hyperbole?

Ⓐ Most famous
Ⓑ Jell-o
Ⓒ Seven flavors
Ⓓ Fruit flavors

20. How does the advertiser reinforce how wonderful Jell-o is?

Ⓐ The woman in the photo asks for all 7 flavors.
Ⓑ The image of the woman seems dreamy, almost like she can't wait for it.
Ⓒ Emphasizes the affordability of it at 10 cents per package.
Ⓓ All of the above.

21.

Determine whether the following statement is True or False.

In the above image the fact that Lincoln is staring directly at the camera, and seems serious gives him a powerful personality by the image alone.

Ⓐ True
Ⓑ False

22. Some creative techniques that are used to best shape the audience's impression of the subject include _____.

Ⓐ Words with strong connotations
Ⓑ Font (emphasizing with big font)
Ⓒ Pictures
Ⓓ All of the above

Answer Key and Detailed Explanations

Chapter 2: Reading: Literature

Down the Rabbit-Hole

Question No.	Answer	Detailed Explanations
1	D	The correct answer is D because she is not interested in her sister's book as it has no conversations in it.
2	C	The correct answer is C because she goes down the hole without any thought about safety.
3	B	The correct answer is B. She has so many connecting thoughts about how things work and are connected as she goes down the hole.
4	B	The correct answer is B. The quote is endearing and the reader can really see into the childlike mind of Alice.
5	B	The correct answer is B because she starts to compare herself to the lens of the telescope and a comparison between two things that uses like is called a simile.
6	C	The correct answer is C The imagery here allows the reader to imagine Alice likes a telescope opening and shutting to view things at a distance.
7	D	The correct answer is D because all of those quotes reflect this childlike characteristic of Alice.
8	B	The correct answer is B because she describes the room including the "Marmalade" jar that she is looking at.
9	A	The correct answer is A. The narrator can easily see inside Alice's head which makes the tale told in 3rd person (using he or she), but because we can not see inside the rabbit's or the sister's head, the view is also considered limited.
10	A	The correct answer is A because it starts with her curiously following the rabbit and ends with her determined to get into the world on the other side.

A Psalm of Life

Question No.	Answer	Detailed Explanations
1	B	The answer is B because the tone throughout is urging and demanding that we have to live meaningful lives.
2	A	The answer is A and can be found in the title of the poem
3	C	The correct answer is C because he is referring to people who are almost sleeplike. He is saying it puts our souls to sleep when we choose not to live life fully.
4	A	The correct answer is A because the quote emphasizes this idea that our actions should make us better each day. That line suggests that we need to spend our days acting and doing, so that tomorrow we are a better person that has grown from that action.
5	B	The correct answer is B, false it doesn't use a metaphor.
6	A	The correct answer is A because that is who the narrator references in stanza 7.
7	A	"A" is story's message. Theme is the main message or big idea of the story.
8		The climax is the end of the conflict and it is through the conflict that the reader will understand what the protagonist learns, which in turn is usually the theme of a piece of literature
9		**A** identify the climax of the story **B** identify the important elements of the plot **C** analyze how the main character grows in the denouement **D** connect the growth of the character to lessons in the real world

Question No.	Answer	Detailed Explanations
10	A	The answer is A, imagery that can shape the impression the reader has about the theme of a story. For example if the author includes symbols in his words to shape the theme, it can make the message more firm about the meaning of the work. For example, the comparison of humans to "cattle" in the above poem uses imagery to emphasize the message of strife and movement as guides for living.

Our story today is called "The Birthmark"

Question No.	Answer	Detailed Explanations
1	B	The answer is B because the protagonist is the main character and the one that undergoes change, and a dynamic character is one that changes and learns over the course of a text.
2	D	The answer is D because he becomes completely focused and obsessed with the birthmark and cannot see anything beyond that.
3	D	The answer is D because he is so obsessed with the birthmark, he cannot see any way around it
4	D	The correct answer is D because he changes through the text and by the end he is left alone with only science, but it isn't enough
5	D	The answer is D because theme, character development, and conflict are all a part of this quote.
6	A	The correct answer is A because it says "Many a gentleman would have risked his life for the honor of kissing that mysterious hand."
7	D	The answer is D because all of those quotes show how fixated Alymer can become on things. If it's not his work, it's the birthmark.
8	B	The correct answer is B because it is because he is obsessed with making her perfect that he loses sight of her as a person, and therefore destroys her
9	D	The correct answer is D because those are all ways that we uncover traits about a character.
10		Any quote that is attributed to Georgiana's thoughts in which she reveals something about Alymer's character. For example: "But she realized then that his mind would forever be on the march, always requiring something newer, better and more perfect."

Hope is the thing with feathers

Question No.	Answer	Detailed Explanations
1	B	The correct answer is B. Denotive is the literal, or exact meaning of a word without any shades of meaning.
2	A	The correct answer is A because the connotative definition of a word is designed to invoke an emotional response to the word
3	B	The connotation of a word is designed to provoke an emotional response, so based on our emotional response to the word, we can analyze the tone of the piece or how the narrator sounds.
4		Answers may vary, but should include the house or piazza, the gardens, the college. These details help you to picture or visualize the story.
5	A	The answer is, True- the words "sore" and "abash" allow the reader to understand the strength of the storm
6	B	The correct answer is B because the speaker seems to want to protect this little bird of hope, and when the storm comes and bashes it, it really emphasizes the aggression of the storm over the idea of hope.
7	A	The answer is A because the speaker is commenting on how this bird never stops singing. She emphasizes – at all- with her dash
8	C	The answer is C, if you are going to be the opposite of the storm that destroys the bird of hope.
9		Personification. Because she is comparing hope to a bird, and therefore is personifying it.
10	A	The correct answer is A because the speaker speaks so beautifully of the importance of hope in the first and last stanza. One can tell that the speaker has had a hard time, but hope has carried her through it.

Richard Cory

Question No.	Answer	Detailed Explanations
1	A	The correct answer is A because that is how the story is presented – exposition is first, followed by rising action which leads to the climax, and then the story starts to fall and there is finally a resolution
2	B	The correct answer is B because really the main issue in the story is Richard Cory shooting himself in the end of the poem. His struggle is internal, as evident by how little the town understands him.
3	D	The correct answer is D because the rising action leads to this point when Richard Cory takes his life. All conflict leads to that surprise.
4	D	The correct answer is D because all those quotes seem to emphasize how superior he is. "We" people; suggests a separateness and "glittered when he walked" and then the direct characterization of him being "rich".
5		The tone used here is a 'matter-of-fact'/ 'calm'/ 'plain' one; which is ironic and also a juxtaposition, because in truth, it is quite shocking that Richard Cory would take his own life.
6		The answer should be True. You can tell this by the way he is described in comparison to Richard and especially in the final stanza when the speaker remarks about how much poorer the people are "And went without the meat, and cursed the bread;"
7	A	The answer is A, True. That is the definition of irony – when what appears to be true isn't and the speaker plays with that. Richard is not as he appears, and his death is in fact ironic.
8	A	The answer is A because parallel plot are when two plots are running simultaneously. In this case, the townspeople are grumbling about not having enough meat, and Richard is in his home shooting himself.

Question No.	Answer	Detailed Explanations
9	A	The correct answer is A because there is a continual reference to "we" and the plight of the people in the town in comparison to Richard's good fortune.
10	D	The correct answer is D. The meat and the bread are simply symbols of the struggles of these townspeople; that they do without.

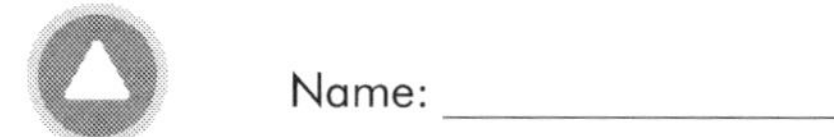

Name: ______________________ Date: ______________

Freedom

Question No.	Answer	Detailed Explanations
1	A	The answer is A because the poet uses "I" to convey his ideas
2	B	

	First-Person	Second-Person	Third-Person Objective	Third-Person	Third-Person Omniscient
When the narrator speaks directly to the reader using you frequently		●			
When the narrator uses he or she to tell the story and reveals the inner motivations of two or more characters					●
When the narrator uses he or she to tell the story but can only reveal one characters thoughts and feelings				●	
When the story is narrated by "I"	●				
When the narrator uses he or she to tell the story but doesn't reveal the inner motivations of the characters			●		

Question No.	Answer	Detailed Explanations
3	A	The correct answer is A. He constantly remarks on their state of "slumber", as though they are sleeping through this oppression.
4	C	The correct answer is C. He compares the lack of movement of his people to a sleeping state, and they are stuck in this night, and almost comfortable there. This comparison does not use like or as, therefore it is a metaphor.
5		The correct answer is D. He makes reference to fear, slumber, and the anarchy of destiny in the poem.
6		This can vary, but students should point to images like: brainless wires, mindless habits, shackles of slumber, etc.
7	D	The correct answer is D. World literature is a portal, from which we can view how other cultures live to improve our own world connectedness.
8	A	The correct answer is A. He feels that they are sleeping and need a wake-up call.
9	A	The correct answer is A. The master of show is whoever is leading the people.
10	B	The correct answer is B. Understanding how we connect and are interdependent is an important part of how we understand ourselves. World literature can teach us more about ourselves as we learn about other cultures.

Name: ______________________ Date: ______________

All The World's A Stage

Question No.	Answer	Detailed Explanations
1	A	The correct answer is A. All other aspects of man are mentioned in the poem.
2	A	The correct answer is A. The tone of this poem is a certain disgust with mankind. The infant is described as "mewling" and the old man has no teeth, eyes, etc. The stages indicate a certain reliance on others, or dependence which the narrator feels is sort of sad.
3	B	The correct answer is B because you can see the round belly and the formal suit. The character as depicted seems to have an air of importance.
4	B	It seems almost circus-like as evident by the monkey, jester, children walking around on stilts, etc.
5	C	The poem unfolds like a story by first describing our "entrances and exits" and then goes on to describe the parts we play in this story.
6	A	The correct answer is A, because in both the stages of mankind are separate, and unique. They don't appear to be connected though they are of the same person
7	B	The answer is B because in the painting you can see that he is almost singing to the women in the window.
8		Answers will vary, but the student should make reference to the idea that the stages of man are varied, and unique.
9		Answers will vary but the student should make reference to the images in the poems or the painting that show this "stage idea"
10	A	The correct answer is A. Both the painting and the poem suggest that we are actors. The painting using actors in a circus, while the poem seems to suggest a similar comic element to mankind

"The Three Little Pigs"

Question No.	Answer	Detailed Explanations
1	D	The answer is D. The adapted characters are the pigs and the wolf. The theme remains the same (protecting oneself), and the antagonist is still the wolf as evident by the words huff and puff.
2		Huff and puff
3		In this version, the pig uses fiberglass which is cheap and readily available, like the hay in the original version.
4	A	The correct answer is A setting. The writer has changed the time and place of the story to a more futuristic setting.
5	E	The answer is E because these are not elements that you would see easily if you set it in New York City in 2011. They would be replaced with other items that are more appropriate to a more modern setting

ANSWER KEY AND DETAILED EXPLANATIONS CHAPTER 3 READING: INFORMATIONAL TEXT

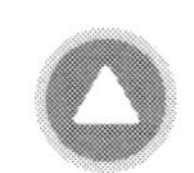

Lower the Voting Age

Question No.	Answer	Detailed Explanations
1	D	The correct answer is D because implicit reading means the reader have to do around to really look at what the writer is trying to say. The ideas are not directly stated
2	B	The correct answer is B because the writer directly states that "she had enough of cleaning up after them"
3	A	The correct answer is A because the writer has noted that she has had enough which suggests she has done this before
4	C	The correct answer is C because Evie cries and hides under the covers.
5	D	The correct answer is D. She lists all of those arguments in the essay
6	D	The answer is D because the writer offers no real evidence to support her point.
7	B	The correct answer is B because she doesn't mention the main points in her conclusion.
8		"While there is an argument that 16 and 17-year-olds are too immature to vote, there is also a danger that they might not vote at all."
9		Students should recognize that the author believes voting must be lowered so young people have more of a voice in politics since they will inherit the problems.
10	B	Evidence supports the reasoning. Reasons are simply opinions, but the evidence grounds that opinion.

Name: ______________________ Date: ______________

Baseball

Question No.	Answer	Detailed Explanations
1	D	The correct answer is D. The essay draws on a variety of topics under the umbrella of baseball
2	C	The correct answer is C. The writer is generalizing all boys which is a hasty generalization.
3	B	The best answer is B because the writer spends about 3 sentences describing the umpire, when the point of the essay is to describe baseball as a sport.
4		It highlights the idea that the student understands the idea of letting go of failure and "shame" She believes that this will be the mark of a successful student.
5	B	The correct answer is B. The writer does not include a topic sentence in that paragraph. The opening sentence does not introduce the main ideas of the paragraph.
6	D	The correct answer is D because the problems with the introduction include all of those flaws. It just seems to be this rambling opening about baseball, without clear direction.
7	D	The answer is D because those are all the reasons we summarize.

Effects of Video Games

<table>
<tr><th>Question No.</th><th>Answer</th><th>Detailed Explanations</th></tr>
<tr><td>1</td><td>A & C</td><td>He says it in the last line "But there is enough evidence for both arguments; video games can be both good and bad for those that play them."</td></tr>
<tr><td>2</td><td>A</td><td>The correct answer is A because it shows the "phenomenon" and the writer presents it as a good thing for our culture.</td></tr>
<tr><td>3</td><td></td><td>In this short answer, students should reference this quote "Parents have opined that video games cause children to socially isolate themselves, has been a cause of obesity, made children insensitive to violence, and in short a waste of time."</td></tr>
<tr><td>4</td><td></td><td>This sentence is called the thesis.</td></tr>
<tr><td>5</td><td></td><td>Answers will vary, but they will have had to choose a piece of evidence from the second to last paragraph. They may choose from "Educational games" or discipline or adult gaming, etc. to support their argument. They will have to explain why it is effective evidence.</td></tr>
<tr><td>6</td><td></td><td>
<table>
<tr><th></th><th>Informative</th><th>Persuasive</th><th>Descriptive</th></tr>
<tr><td>Come down to Bill's Auto and get your red hot deal today</td><td></td><td>●</td><td></td></tr>
<tr><td>Today the average person eats his/her weight in sugar every year</td><td>●</td><td></td><td></td></tr>
<tr><td>The dark house stood aloof and lonely at the edge of a crumbling hillside.</td><td></td><td></td><td>●</td></tr>
</table>
</td></tr>
<tr><td>7</td><td>A</td><td>The answer is A because the writer presents a balanced argument.</td></tr>
<tr><td>8</td><td>B</td><td>The correct answer is B because Pokemon is presented in a positive light and described as a "cultural phenomenon".</td></tr>
</table>

Question No.	Answer	Detailed Explanations
9	D	The correct answer is D because personification is used when the house 'stands' and the rest are all true.
10		Topic sentence Supporting sentence #1 Supporting sentence #2 Supporting sentence #3 Clincher

Name: ______________________ Date: ______________

Patrick Henry Speech (March 23, 1775)

Question No.	Answer	Detailed Explanations
1	A	One can assume it means large and powerful because the enemy appears so great judging by the urgency of his tone and the lengths he is going to, to persuade the people to fight.
2	A	The answer is A because sarcasm is the use of irony to emphasize disgust for a subject.
3	B	He wants his people to rise up and revolt against the British rule.
4	B	He uses B, metaphor, to compare life under British rule to slavery. He says by not fighting we purchase peace, but the price is chains. This is a comparison between two ideas.
5	C	The answer is C because both are true
6	A	The correct answer is A because all three are used. Hyperbole is exaggerated language, and the chains are exaggerated. The metaphor is the chains as compared to their "enslavement" to the British.
7		Answers will vary but students want to say words like determined or passionate or angry or revolutionary.
8		figurative
9		connotative
10		tone
11		Logos
12		Pathos
13		Ethos

Question No.	Answer	Detailed Explanations
14		The correct answer is pathos. He is attempting to persuade the audience by appealing to their emotions or heart. He tries to make the audience fearful with statements like "The war is actually begun! The next gale that sweeps from the north will bring to our ears the clash of resounding arms"
15	A	The writer is using A because he is using himself as a motivating force, so it gives him credibility as a speaker which is ethos and then the pathos is in the language which is meant to stir the people into action and demand their freedom.
16	A	The answer is A and while C could be considered an answer, A is your best choice because a rhetorical questioning involves asking a question where the answer is obvious and merely is used as a device to emphasize the ineptness of the counter argument.

John F Kennedy
John F Kennedy's inaugural address in 1961

Question No.	Answer	Detailed Explanations
1	A	The correct answer choice is "A". Metaphor is a figure of speech which compares two things that are unrelated based on common characteristics. The figure of speech used in this sentence is a metaphor.
2		(see below)

	Personification	Overstatment	Symbol
Let both sides unite to heed in all corners of the earth the command of Isaiah--to "undo the heavy burdens . . . (and) let the oppressed go free.		●	
a celebration of freedom--symbolizing an end as well as a beginning--signifying renewal as well as change.			●
this Hemisphere intends to remain the master of its own house.	●		

"Let both sides unite to heed in all corners of the earth the command of Isaiah--to "undo the heavy burdens . . . (and) let the oppressed go free."

This is an overstatement because it is impossible to unite all corners of the world.

A symbol is a figure of speech where something is used to represent something else.

Here, "a celebration of freedom--symbolizing an end as well as a beginning--signifying renewal as well as change.", the celebration of freedom is made to represent a new beginning as well as the end of something else.

Question No.	Answer	Detailed Explanations
3	B	The correct answer is B. Synecdoche is a part of speech where a part represents a whole or a whole represents a part.
4	A	The correct answer is A because that is the definition
5		American Citizens
6	A	While A could be a possibility because it is mentioned in the excerpt, the purpose of the speech is to inform the citizens of America about his intentions as a leader and how he intends to work for the progress of the country.
7	D	The answer is D. The speech was made at the height of cold war, and the tone of the speech depicts strength, compassion, hope, and the belief that Americans working together can achieve growth and progress the country.
8		Answers can vary. But the answers mainly need to emphasize how it is a call for all fellow Americans to work for the greater good of the country instead of only questioning about their rights.
9		Answers can vary. It can include issues that the world faced such as war, revolution, cold war and arms race. The coming together of nations as allies in fighting various nations etc.

President Lincoln Speech

Question No.	Answer	Detailed Explanations
1	A	While A could be a possibility because it is mentioned in the excerpt, the purpose of the speech is to dedicate the ground to the soldiers "We have come to dedicate a portion of that field, as a final resting-place for those who here gave their lives"
2	D	The answer is D because he is very respectful of the soldiers who gave their lives, but he also sounds a little worried about the future of the country. He questions whether or not it will even survive this war.
3	A	The correct answer is A because he emphasizes the sacredness of the soldiers who "struggled" when he says the land is already consecrated.
4	B	This correct answer is B because a primary source comes straight from the main source of information, whereas a secondary source is a take on the primary source.
5		This is true because it is an excerpt of the actual speech not a commentary on the speech (that would be considered a secondary source)

Name: ______________________ Date: ______________

Can bullying be overcome by Kindness

Question No.	Answer	Detailed Explanations
1	B	The correct answer is B, logical fallacy
2	D	The correct answer is D because these are all different types of logical fallacies
3	B	The answer is B because it is about connecting ideas in an illogical way
4	C	The answer is C because the article offers no real proof to make the generalization that kindness leads to those three things. There might be other factors that lead to this result.
5		Answers can vary, but must include an opposing argument. For example: "Unfortunately, in many schools, negative behaviors such as bullying results in punishment which is thought to reduce this kind of behavior in future." Referencing the zero-tolerance is the counter argument to teaching kindness, and the author debunks its value in the next sentence. This is why it is the counter argument
6		Answers can vary, but it is anything from the bullet pointed list: Mindfulness, SEL, etc.
7		This is false, this is not the writer's thesis. She doesn't discuss how to reward kindness at all in the essay nor does she focus on modeling kindness. This is why it can't be her thesis though the writer might think it is.
8		Hasty generalization
9		Ad hominem
10		Straw man

ANSWER KEY AND DETAILED EXPLANATIONS CHAPTER 4: LANGUAGE STANDARDS

Grammar and Usage

Question No.	Answer	Detailed Explanations
1	C	C because by the birthday cake describes the verb placed.
2	D	D because while I finish making the dough is a dependent clause that modifies the verb. It is a clause as opposed to a phrase because it contains both a subject and a predicate.
3	D	D because extremely expensive is an adjective phrase; extremely describes the degree to which the present was expensive.
4	A	A because it could stand on its own as a complete sentence with its own subject and predicate.
5	D	D because a relative clause is not a complete sentence and it gives extra information about the preceding noun.
6	B	B because a comma separates the dependent clause starting with Rosa Parks's refusal to sit in the back of the bus from the independent clause the Montgomery bus boycott brought national attention to the issue of segregation.
7		"of the people, by the people, for the people" because the three prepositional phrases match in length and structure.
8		You should revise your essay to use a variety of sentence structures to add interest. A variety of sentence lengths and structures will make your writing sound more natural, rather than choppy and stilted. To accomplish this, you could combine sentences or change sentences that start with the same word. For example, you might write "William Shakespeare wrote his famous play, Hamlet, in 1599."

Question No.	Answer	Detailed Explanations
9		(see table and explanation below)

Sentence	Write the phrases	Type of phrases
Siggy enjoys baking cupcakes and watching movies.	Watching Movies	verb phrases
That celebrity is famous for her brilliant acting and sensational dancing.	brilliant acting	adjective phrases
Darlene looked for her lost kitten under the couch, in the basement, and behind the dresser.	behind the dresser	prepositional phrases

Baking cupcakes and watching movies are verb phrases because they both begin with a verb and they match each other structurally. Sensational dancing and brilliant acting are adjective phrases because they both begin with an adjective and match each other structurally. Under the couch, in the basement, and behind the dresser are prepositional phrases because they all begin with a preposition and match each other structurally.

Question No.	Answer
10	A

	Yes	No
Scientists have reported the discovery of a new exoplanet that orbits a star outside the solar system.	●	
Named Ross 128b and considered a temperate planet.		●
Its temperate climate means that it is just warm enough for liquid water to exist on its surface.	●	
Could Ross 128b sustain life? Scientists don't yet know.	●	

Command of Capitalization, Punctuation, and Spelling

Question No.	Answer	Detailed Explanations
1	B	B because it is a contraction meaning they are.
2	A	A because it introduces a list of items.
3	A	A because a colon can only combine two independent clauses and only when the second further explains the first.
4	B	B because it separates two independent clauses.
5	D	D because it means extremely which is the best fit for the context of the sentence; to indicates direction; two is a number; and toe is a part of the body.
6	C	C because it separates the dependent clause, 'Soon after moving to a new house', from the independent clause, 'Thomas and Denny made friends with their neighbors'.
7		Mark did not study for the final exam; therefore, he will probably not pass the test.
8		East High School proudly presents the award winning musical Bye Bye Birdie. This family-friendly show will run for one weekend only. Filled with explosive tap dance numbers, Bye Bye Birdie is a musical performance not to be missed!

Question No.	Answer	Detailed Explanations		
9			First Mark	Second Mark
		Mary Kate screamed at the top of her lungs. __If I don't see that room cleaned by the end of the day__ there will be hell to pay!"	" quotation mark	, comma
		James Joyce's Ulysses is considered one of the finest works of modernist fiction published__ however__ publication was made difficult for editors due to errors purposefully included by the author	; semicolon	, comma
		Father has brought several different kinds of vegetables from the store__ carrots, celery, and beets. Which would you prefer__	: colon	? question mark
		Martin Luther King Jr.'s "Letter from Birmingham Jail" lists circumstances which African Americans have had to cope with. King writes, "When you have seen vicious mobs lynch your mothers and fathers at will and drown your sisters and brothers at whim__ when you have seen hate-filled policemen curse, kick, brutalize, and even kill your black brothers and sisters with impunity__" and so on, to foster empathy among readers.	; semicolon	... elipsis

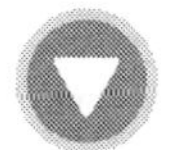

Name: ______________________ Date: ______________

Question No.	Answer	Detailed Explanations
10		(see table below)

	Correct	Incorrect
definitely	●	
occasionally		●
publically		●
accidentally	●	

Functions of Language

Question No.	Answer	Detailed Explanations
1	C	C because the author's last name and then first name are listed first in the Works Cited entry.
2	D	D because The New York Times, the title of a newspaper, is listed in the source title position in the Works Cited entry.
3	C	C because the date accessed is not included in the MLA citation of a printed journal article; all other information listed is available in the Works Cited entry.
4	B	B because graceful is the opposite of awkward just as excruciating is the opposite of mild.
5	A	A because gasoline is stored in a tank just as money is stored in a vault.
6	B	B because obvious and conspicuous are synonymous just as astonishing and thrilling are synonymous.
7		To plagiarize is to use the original author's exact words as if they are your own without using an accurate citation. Paraphrasing means to put information into your own original words.
8		An encyclopedia article about the Trail of Tears would be purely factual and objective. Its purpose would be only to inform the reader about the facts of the event like the dates. The first-hand account of the Trail of Tears would be personal and subjective. Its purpose would be to show the Native American perspective of the event; it would reflect the feelings of the people who were forced to endure the Trail of Tears.

Question No.	Answer	Detailed Explanations
9		

Common Verb	Precise Verb
"Shhh!" Melanie said. "Be quiet or you will wake up Mom and Dad.".	whispered
"Touch down! The North High football team has just won the state championship!" said the announcer.	exclaimed
"Can you please help me to clean up the classroom?" said the teacher.	pleaded

Question No.	Answer	Detailed Explanations
10		

	Formal	Informal
What's up, Jose? How you doin' to-day?.		●
I hear what you are saying, but I must respectfully dis-agree.	●	
I am calling to in-form you that I have scheduled your interview for next week.	●	
Whoa, did you see the trick that kid did on his skateboard? He's got mad skills!		●

Informal language is conversational and may contain slang or contractions, as with What's up, doin', whoa, and mad skills. Formal language is academic and sophisticated, as with inform and respectfully.

Determining Unknown Words

Question No.	Answer	Detailed Explanations
1	A	A because disseminate means to spread or disperse.
2	B	B because dissidents means protesters or dissenters.
3	C	C because facilitate means to make easier or to enable.
4	C	C because re- means to do something again, as in to say again, name again, or build again.
5	A	A because un- means not or lacking, as in not finished, not skilled, and not friendly.
6	D	D because -ish means having the quality of or being similar to, as in to be like a child, to be like a snob, and to have the quality of style.
7	D	I can infer that a benevolent person is probably good and kind because the root word bene meaning good is in the word benevolent.
8		A dictionary can provide the pronunciation of the word; this will help her to read it out loud correctly. A dictionary entry can also give the part of speech; this will help her to use the word correctly in her own writing. A dictionary entry can also offer synonyms; this can help her to understand the meaning of the word better.

Question No.	Answer	Detailed Explanations
9		

Word	Part of Speech
White House	Noun
we	Pronoun
disappear	verb
carefully	adverb
and	conjunction
dirty	adjectives

Nouns name a person, place or thing; pronouns take the place of nouns; verbs show action; adverbs describe verbs; conjunctions combine phrases and clauses; adjectives describe nouns.

10

	Adjective	Adverb
It was a hot afternoon.	○	
It was a terribly hot afternoon.		○
The afternoon sun was terribly hot.	○	

Hot is an adjective describing afternoon; terribly is an adverb describing the adjective hot; afternoon is an adjective describing sun.

Figurative Language

Question No.	Answer	Detailed Explanations
1	B	B because hyperbole is an exaggeration used for emphasis.
2	D	D because a metaphor draws a direct comparison between two objects; in this case, the author states that there is literally a dark cloud over the girl's head when describing her sadness.
3	C	C because an allusion is a reference to a famous work that is easily identifiable by the reader.
4	A	Anwer is A, because the pepper is a non-human object being given human qualities – the ability to tickle.
5	B	B because a euphemism is a phrase that is milder or less harsh than another word or phrase.
6	A	A because an oxymoron is formed when two opposite words are paired to create a new phrase.
7		The connotation of "house" is neutral; it means a shelter. The connotation of "home" is positive; it implies a safe, loving place where a family lives.
8		Students should explain that the connotation of the two words affects how and when they are used. "Slender" has a positive connotation that implies a person is slim in a healthy and attractive way. For example, Sheila was proud of her slender frame which was the result of exercising diligently and eating a balanced diet. However, "Gaunt" has a negative connotation that implies a person is too thin and unhealthy. For example, the refugees were gaunt after weeks with very little food.

Question No.	Answer	Detailed Explanations
9		Alliteration: What, Sledges, Merriment / World, Silver, Melody The repeated consonant sound of M in merriment and melody represent alliteration.
10		See table below. The second excerpt demonstrates assonance, or the repetition of a vowel sound within nearby words, in the phrase "radiant maiden". The third excerpt demonstrates assonance in the phrase "purple curtain".

Question 9

Alliteration	
What	World
Sledges	Silver
Merriment	Melody

Question 10

	Yes	No
"Once upon a midnight dreary"		
"For the rare and radiant maiden whom the angels name Lenore."		●
"And the silken, sad, uncertain rustling of each purple curtain"	●	

Academic and Domain-Specific Vocabulary

Question No.	Answer	Detailed Explanations
1	D	D because economy means the wealth and resources of a country.
2	B	B because legislative means relating to laws or the making of them.
3	A	A because analysis means an examination or investigation of something
4	B	B because concepts means abstract ideas or notions.
5	C	C because evidence means the available facts or information.
6	A	A because infer means to deduce or conclude.
7		To paraphrase the student should capture the entire passage and express it in new language. For example, "President Barack Obama believes that Americans need to be responsible for making the changes in the world that they believe in, rather than waiting for someone else to do it."
8		To summarize, the student's response should be shorter than the original text, be written in the student's own words, and capture the central idea of the passage. For example, 'The central idea of this passage is that humans are adversely affecting the environment, causing an imbalance in earth's ecosystems. Humans need to implement sustainable practices to avoid damage from which the earth can not recover.'

Question No.	Answer	Detailed Explanations
9		

Sentence	Correct Word
The scientists uncovered a bone that was (approximately/appropriately) one foot long.	approximately
Sean's greatest (arbitrary/attribute) is his ability to always see the good in everyone.	attribute
The starting gun signaled that the track race was about to (commence/compensate).	commence
Nicole planned to (compile/comprehensive) all of her data into a report for her boss.	compile

Question No.	Answer	Detailed Explanations
10		

	Correct	Incorrect
Despite his strong feelings about the case, the judge had to remain objective and fair when hearing both sides of the argument.	●	
The gardener showed his ambiguity towards his work when he cut corners and put forth little effort.		●
Zeus, Hera, and Poseidon are some of the main characters in Greek mythology.	●	
The first chapters of a book usually includes expository information to fill in the reader on essential background knowledge.	●	

Objective means unbiased and is used correctly as an adjective describing the judge; ambiguity means uncertainty and is used incorrectly; mythology refers to the set of stories and beliefs of a particular group of people and is used correctly as a noun referring to Greek mythology; expository refers to a text's exposition or background information and is used correctly.

Answer Key and Detailed Explanations Chapter 5: Writing Standards

Write arguments to support claims

Question No.	Answer	Detailed Explanations
1		Thesis
2		Answers can vary, but must include some form of 1) pre-writing/brainstorming/metal mapping, 2) drafting 3) revising 4) proofreading 5) publishing
3	D	The correct answer is D because all of those parts are in a traditional paragraph
4	C	The correct answer is C because the three points addressed in the thesis correspond to the three supporting body paragraphs that follow the introduction.
5	C	The correct answer is C because the thesis should be the last line of your introduction
6	D	The correct answer is D because the topic sentence should link back to the thesis and explain how that paragraph supports the thesis.
7	A	The answer is A because it avoids using "I" and it is a complete thought that explains what the essay will be about.
8	A	The correct answer is A because these are the connecting words in writing. Words such as in a similar way or likewise can be used to emphasize comparisons
9	A	The correct answer is A because one must be able to prove the opinion to support the argument
10	D	The correct answer is D because you have to do all of those things to write your argument effectively.

Name: ____________________ Date: ____________

Write informative/explanatory texts

Question No.	Answer	Detailed Explanations
1	D	The correct answer is D because the rest are all false. Writing to inform and explain is about choosing important facts and then developing your writing around that. Opinion has little place in an informative piece, and images can and should be used to support your paper.
2	B	The correct answer is B because facts are central to an informative piece of writing.
3	D	The correct answer is D because they all will inform the reader of something
4	B	The correct answer is B. Informational texts should use some bullet points, so the reader can see the information more easily
5		The answer is false. This type of writing would be called persuasive because the writer is using hyperbole
6		The correct answer is True, because this essay will inform the reader of the different types of creatures in the forest.
7	D	The correct answer is D because maps, diagrams, and lists are all characteristics of informational writing
8	B	The correct answer is B. When an informational text uses steps, that type of writing uses a sequence of events.
9	A	The answer is A because you will need transitions like more, then, next, first to move from one step to the next.
10	D	The correct answer is D because those are all strategies so you can group information to begin to write the organized piece.

Write narratives

Question No.	Answer	Detailed Explanations
1		See matching table below
2		Answers should include key terms like setting, character (protagonist/antagonist), theme, etc.
3		See table below
4	C	The correct answer is C. First person is when the narrator uses I. For example "I was walking down the street, when I saw it."
5	D	The correct answer is D. A dynamic character is one that grows and learns from the conflict by definition
6	B	The correct answer is B because quotes are used to offset dialogue from the narrative around it.

Question 1:

A	B
Series of events in a story	Plot
The source of tension in the story	Conflict
The beginning of a story when the characters and setting are introduced	exposition

Question 3:

	After the climax and before the resolution	**Before the climax and after the exposition**	**The moment of greatest intensity in the story**
Rising action		●	
Falling action	●		
Climax			●

Question No.	Answer	Detailed Explanations
7	A	The correct answer is A because setting is defined as time and place of the story
8	A	The correct answer is A because first you set up the story with background information (exposition), then the action rises until the climax when it begins to fall and then you have the resolution or how the climax is fixed
9	B	The correct answer is B. The inciting incident is what causes the action to rise
10	B	The answer is B because that is where the rising action peaks and then starts to fall. Usually the moment of greatest emotional intensity in the story.

Name: ______________________ Date: ______________

Produce clear and coherent writing

Question No.	Answer	Detailed Explanations
1		See table below
2		Persuasive writing uses hyperbole, or exaggerated speech to make a point
3		For this answer, students want to reference bold font, bullet points, slides, images, and any other organizational device to manage information
4		See table below

Question 1

	Persuasive writing	Informational writing	Narrative writing
Writing that uses bullet points, graphs, and images to tell the reader about a particular topic		●	
Writing that is designed to convince the reader of the writer's point	●		
A style of writing that includes plot and character			●

Question 4

A	B
A letter from a child to his mother explaining why King Charles Cavalier is the best.	Persuasive
A pamphlet about the different types of cocker spaniels.	Informational
A fictional story about a dog named George and his owner Evie.	Narrative

Question No.	Answer	Detailed Explanations
5	A	The answer is A because you would tell a story using metaphors and sensory details (details that try to get the reader to see, smell, hear, taste, and touch)
6	A	The answer is A because you would persuade them to do something about the waste
7	C	The answer is C because the writer is using hyperbole to get you to visit Costa Rica. Words like wonderful and amazing are a red flag to the reader that you are being persuaded.
8	D	The correct answer is D because these are all types of informational texts. Sequence is a list of information and B and C deal with informing the reader of problems /causes and solutions/effects.
9	B	The correct answer is B because the last sentence, which is the thesis, says: "While there is an argument that 16 and 17-year-olds are too immature to vote, there is also a danger that they might not vote at all.
10	B	The answer is B. You can tell this because the writer hints that it is because the voting age is 18, teenagers may never become voters, and that is the problem.

Develop and strengthen writing

Question No.	Answer	Detailed Explanations
1		A Drafting B. Revising C. Proofreading D. Planning E. Publishing
2		Answers can vary but should include the idea that the process allows you to edit the information you are sharing so you can choose your structure and organization correctly and proofread. This allows your ideas to be read more clearly.
3		Students might be apt to write drafting here, but the correct answer is revising. This is the point in which they take the raw thoughts from the draft and shape it into something stronger.
4		The answer is false, because the stage you focus in on punctuation and capitalization is proofreading.
5	C	The correct answer is C because all of the punctuation is correct in that one. In the first one, it should end in a ?, which eliminates a and b, and in the last one, the writer has created a fragment by putting a period after voting.
6	D	The correct answer is D because the writer can do all of those things
7	D	The answer is D because the words are all correct
8	C	The correct answer is C and the dependent clause is Because I love dogs.
9		This answer is false. The writer should not even be drafting using informal language. That can appear in the pre-write, but by the time the writing is in drafting, the language should be more formal.
10	B	The answer is B. Your writing has to have different types of sentences in it so the writing is varied and the reader stays interested.

Use technology to produce, publish, and update writing products

Question No.	Answer	Detailed Explanations
1	C	The correct answer is C because plagiarism is defined as stealing from a source without giving that source credit.
2	A	The correct answer is A. When you cite your sources correctly you inform the reader of where you gathered the information from
3		Paraphrasing is borrowing the idea, but not the words and yes, you do need to cite it.
4	D	The correct answer is D because these are the defining characteristics of a good research statement.
5	D	The correct answer is D because those are all different styles.
6	A	The correct answer is A because you would place your source in a separate section of your paper.
7	B	The correct answer is B because you should place all direct quotes in quotation marks, unless the quote is longer than 4 lines. In that case, you would follow a different pattern
8	D	The correct answer is D (B and C only). Websites ending in .org or .edu are not commercial and therefore not necessarily trying to persuade you. The information provided on those sites is more informational
9		Wikipedia is not a good source to use because it is a wiki and can be edited by various people, making it an unreliable source
10	D	The answer is D. You should use one strategy to catalogue your research for easy access

Name: ______________________ Date: ______________

Conduct short and sustained research project

Question No.	Answer	Detailed Explanations
1	B	The correct answer is B because you should vary your sources so they include both print and non-print resources.
2		The answer is True because it's focused on an effect and an age, so it is narrow and specific
3	B	The correct answer is B because you set up your question after brainstorming on the topic a bit.
4		This student has to make reference to the fact that the topic is too broad and too general, and the research question should really focus the writer, so they can research more directly.
5	B	The correct answer is B because you need various pieces of evidence to support a topic, but in a smaller paper, you really don't want more than three sources so you are able to integrate your information with the research.
6	A	The correct answer is A because the other 3 deal with other aspects of the research process
7		A.Proofread B. Publish C. Brainstorm topics D. Group/Organize research making connections E. Draft F. Revise G. Research, choosing applicable sources H. Craft a research question
8		Write a research question
9	D	The correct answer is none of the above because all of those things must be included in your bibliography or works cited.
10	A	The correct answer is A because those are the most valid types of sites.

Source-Based Writing

Question No.	Answer	Detailed Explanations
1	D	D because the official site of the science museum will offer the most accurate, detailed, and up-to-date information needed for planning the field trip.
2	A	A because it follows the rules for proper MLA format.
3	A	A because any one performance's quality is based on taste more than fact; the other three statements are facts.
4	B	B because the statistics will be numerically accurate and they are from a government agency.
5	D	D because the statement has nothing to do with the flowers symbolizing innocence.
6	D	D because it follows the rules of proper MLA formatting.
7		No, it is not plagiarized because the student used information from the original source text but put it into his/her own words. None of the original phrases from the source have been 'lifted', or passed off as the student's work.
8		"American wars" is a weak search term because it is too general. "American" could refer to North or South America; it could include wars that were fought in the U.S. or wars that were fought elsewhere but included the U.S. A stronger search term would be "causes of the Civil War" because it specifically indicates the topic and what the student needs to know about the topic.

Name: ______________________ Date: ______________

Question No.	Answer	Detailed Explanations
9		

Sentence	Correct word
Of all the information, quotes, and data points that could be used in an academic paper, an effective writer must (assess/accurately) which should be used based on the research question.	Assess
(Assessment/Authoritative) sources are those that are connected to well known and respected publishers, universities, newspapers, journals, and authors.	Authoritative
To ensure that the paper is balanced and unbiased, an effective writer must be cautious of (overreliance/paraphrasing) on just one source.	Overreliance
An effective writer must have a clear, focused research question in order to find the most (relevant/relatable) information that addresses the topic of study.	Relevant

10

	Correct	Incorrect
Smith stated that the habit of slouching over a computer will have long-term effects on one's posture and spinal health. (263).		●
No other musician "has had as much influence on the music industry" (Johnston 322).	●	
Harriet Gladwell explains that in those days, women were unable to own property, enter into contracts, or earn a salary (Gladwell, "Women and Power").		●

Question No.	Answer	Detailed Explanations
		A bibliographic citation should include the author's last name, a comma, then the page number within parentheses. The period should be on the outside of the parentheses at the end of the sentence.

Name: ________________ Date: __________

Citing Text-Evidence

Question No.	Answer	Detailed Explanations
1	D	D because the passage both persuades the reader of the benefits of a later school start time and supports that claim with general factual information.
2	D	D because it captures the main idea of the entire passage.
3	B	B because the color and sound words appeal to the reader's sense of sight and sound.
4	C	C because it summarizes the most important idea conveyed throughout the entire passage.
5	B	B because "predetermined" means fixed or prearranged.
6	A	A because the text refers to the circle of life, the "road of Destiny", and one's predetermined fortune which all support the theme that one's past is part of his/her present.
7		The two houses differ in that one is run-down and old while the other is large and luxurious. The author describes the first as "bare and shabby" and the other as "stately" and "well-kept".
8		Troy's claim that "dogs offer emotional support" does not have sufficient evidence to support it. Troy supported his claim about the physical benefits of dog ownership with multiple pieces of evidence from an authoritative source. To strengthen his claim that dog ownership benefits humans emotionally too, he will need more evidence from a credible source. This is important because it proves that his claim is not merely an opinion but is supported by other relevant evidence and trustworthy sources."

Question No.	Answer	Detailed Explanations
9		

reasons for not voting	rank
Out of town	3
Not interested	2
Bad weather conditions	5
Forgot to vote	4
Too busy	1

"Too busy" was answered by 2[illegible] ested" by 16%, "out of town" by 10%, "forgot to vote" by 8%, and "bad weather conditions" by less than 1% of the population.

10

	Supported by Cartoon	Not Supported by Cartoon
Women were an important part of the war effort.	●	
Dogs were an important part of the war effort.		●
Common home goods could be recycled into items needed by the military.	●	
Americans should be suspicious of Japanese, Russians, and Italians		●

Dogs were pictured on the poster but were not part of the message. While the Japanese, Russians, and Italians were America's enemies during World War II, they are not mentioned on the poster. The other statements are referenced by the images and text on the poster.

Additional Practice Questions

Question No.	Answer	Detailed Explanations
1	B	The correct answer is B. This is called an adaptation of a piece of literature, when you transform an original text into another setting or style.
2	A	The answer is A. If a novel is converted to a movie, it is considered an adaptation of the novel because it is turned into a new form.
3	D	The answer is D. All of those might be clues that the story has been adapted from another source
4	B	The answer is B. Any time a novel is rewritten into another genre, that is considered an adaptation
5	C	The correct answer is C (both A and B). The adaptations can allow you to understand something that you might not have understood in the original.
6	B	The correct answer is B because the reader has to know the thesis in order to be able to identify the ways the writer presents the work.
7	D	The correct choice is D because the others are simply level 1 analysis that don't require implicit reading
8	D	The correct answer choice is D because the writer has to be sure that the evidence is connected to the point and cite his/her sources
9	B	The correct answer is B because the other 3 might highlight some of the ideas of the article, but Pip's story ties into how we can grow through the study of his character.
10	B	While you could argue that B could be an answer, the answer is c because the focus of the short article is on how literature can help a person to grow not actually on the writer herself
11	A	The correct answer is A because while the rest are true, when it comes to developing an essay you should always have a topic sentence and supporting details that support it

Question No.	Answer	Detailed Explanations
12	A	The answer is A, because that is the sentence that the entire essay revolves around.
13	D	The correct answer is D because the study of multimedia can help us understand all of those things and can deepen our critical/ analytical skills about how information is presented
14	B	The answer is B, because it is a reprint of a "Washington Times" article.
15		Answers can vary, but the language used in the headline, really emphasises the turmoil that came with going to war. The image show a more orderly acceptance of the war, but the headline uses the word "turmoil" which enhances the chaos of the entry into the war.
16	D	The correct answer is D. The newspaper is sympathizing with the Austrians and their assinated duke as evident by those above three points – the headline, the photos, and lastly the subheading.
17		The answer is true. The objective of multimedia is to present a certain subject in a particular light, thereby engaging the audience emotionally to sway their point of view.
18		The answer is "audience". Multimedia manipulates images and words, to best suit their audience and to engage the audience.

Question No.	Answer	Detailed Explanations
19		Hyperbole is the exaggeration of language often used in multumedia design. The answer is a because it may or it might not be the "most famous", but the fact that the writer uses most indicates the use of hyperbole
20	D	The answer is D, because all of those are ploys by the advertiser to get the audience to want Jell-O
21		The answer is true. A photographer makes choices, and the fact that Abraham Lincoln is staring dead at the camera, and it is only a headshot, makes him seem more powerful. A full body shot, or a picture that included background, would lose this powerful effect.
22	D	The correct answer is D. All of those are techniques used by a writer of multimedia to enhance the impression of their subject.

Notes

Additional Information

High School ELA 2 FAQs

What will ELA 2 Assessment Look Like?

In many ways, the ELA 2 assessments will be unlike anything many students have ever seen. The tests require students to complete tasks to assess a deeper understanding of the domains such as Reading Literature, Reading Informational Text, Language, Writing sections.

What are the English Language Arts credit programs offered in High Schools?

Most of the High Schools offer ELA 1, ELA 2, ELA 3 programs.

What item types are included in the Online ELA 2 Test?

Because the assessment is online, the test will consist of a combination of new types of questions:

1. Drag and Drop
2. Drop Down
3. Essay Response
4. Extended Constructed Response
5. Hot Text Select and Drag
6. Hot Text Selective Highlight
7. Matching Table In-line
8. Matching Table Single Response
9. Multiple Choice – Single Correct Response, radial buttons
10. Multiple Choice – Multiple Response, check boxes
11. Numeric Response
12. Short Text
13. Table Fill-in

Discover Engaging and Relevant Learning Resources

Lumos EdSearch is a safe search engine specifically designed for teachers and students. Using EdSearch, you can easily find thousands of standards-aligned learning resources such as questions, videos, lessons, worksheets, and apps. Teachers can use EdSearch to create custom resource kits to perfectly match their lesson objective and assign them to one or more students in their classroom.

To access the EdSearch tool, use the search box after you log into Lumos StepUp or use the link provided below.

www.lumoslearning.com/a/edsearchb	

The Lumos Standards Coherence map provides information about previous level, next level, and related standards. It helps educators and students visually explore learning standards. It's an effective tool to help students progress through the learning objectives. Teachers can use this tool to develop their own pacing charts and lesson plans. Educators can also use the coherence map to get deep insights into why a student is struggling in a specific learning objective.

Teachers can access the Coherence maps after logging into the StepUp Teacher Portal or use the link provided below.

www.lumoslearning.com/a/coherence-map	

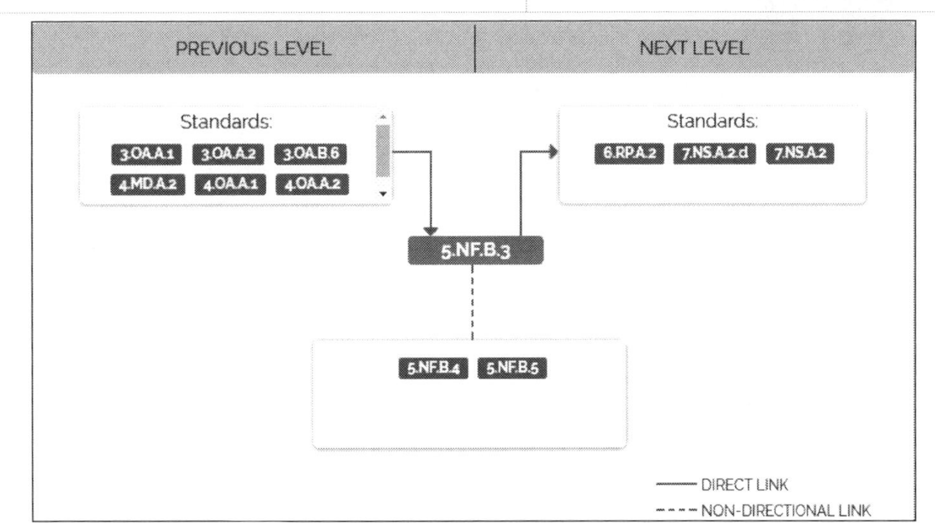

Progress Chart

Passage/ Lesson	Lesson/Passage Name	Q No.	Page No.	Practice		Mastered	Re-practice /Reteach
				Date	Score		
Chapter 2	Reading: Literature		8				
Passage 1	Down The Rabbit Hole		8				
		1					
		2					
		3					
		4					
		5					
		6					
		7					
		8					
		9					
		10					
Passage 2	A Psalm of Life		14				
		1					
		2					
		3					
		4					
		5					
		6					
		7					
		8					
		9					
		10					
Passage 3	Our story today is called "The Birthmark"		18				
		1					
		2					
		3					
		4					
		5					
		6					

Passage/ Lesson	Lesson/Passage Name	Q No.	Page No.	Practice		Mastered	Re-practice /Reteach
				Date	Score		
		7					
		8					
		9					
		10					
Passage 4	Hope is the thing with feathers		24				
		1					
		2					
		3					
		4					
		5					
		6					
		7					
		8					
		9					
		10					
Passage 5	Richard Cory		27				
		1					
		2					
		3					
		4					
		5					
		6					
		7					
		8					
		9					
		10					

Passage/ Lesson	Lesson/Passage Name	Q No.	Page No.	Practice		Mastered	Re-practice /Reteach
				Date	Score		
Passage 6	Freedom		30				
		1					
		2					
		3					
		4					
		5					
		6					
		7					
		8					
		9					
		10					
Passage 7	All the world's a stage		35				
		1					
		2					
		3					
		4					
		5					
		6					
		7					
		8					
		9					
		10					
Passage 8	The Three Little Pigs		39				
		1					
		2					
		3					
		4					
		5					

Passage/ Lesson	Lesson/Passage Name	Q No.	Page No.	Practice		Mastered	Re-practice /Reteach
				Date	Score		
Chapter 3	Reading: Informational Text		41				
Passage 1	Lower the Voting Age		41				
		1					
		2					
		3					
		4					
		5					
		6					
		7					
		8					
		9					
		10					
Passage 2	Baseball		46				
		1					
		2					
		3					
		4					
		5					
		6					
		7					
		8					
		9					
		10					

Passage/ Lesson	Lesson/Passage Name	Q No.	Page No.	Practice		Mastered	Re-practice /Reteach
				Date	Score		
Passage 3	Effects Of Video Game		49				
		1					
		2					
		3					
		4					
		5					
		6					
		7					
		8					
		9					
		10					
Passage 4	Patrick Henry Speech		52				
		1					
		2					
		3					
		4					
		5					
		6					
		7					
		8					
		9					
		10					
		11					
		12					
		13					
		14					
		15					
		16					

Passage/ Lesson	Lesson/Passage Name	Q No.	Page No.	Practice		Mastered	Re-practice /Reteach
				Date	Score		
Passage 5	John F Kennedy		57				
		1					
		2					
		3					
		4					
		5					
		6					
		7					
		8					
		9					
Passage 6	President Lincoln Speech		63				
		1					
		2					
		3					
		4					
		5					
Passage 7	Can bullying be overcome by Kindness		65				
		1					
		2					
		3					
		4					
		5					
		6					
		7					
		8					
		9					
		10					

Passage/ Lesson	Lesson/Passage Name	Q No.	Page No.	Practice		Mastered	Re-practice /Reteach
				Date	Score		
Chapter 4	Language		69				
Lesson 1	Grammar and Usage		69				
		1					
		2					
		3					
		4					
		5					
		6					
		7					
		8					
		9					
		10					
Lesson 2	Command of Capitalization, Punctuation, and Spelling		73				
		1					
		2					
		3					
		4					
		5					
		6					
		7					
		8					
		9					
		10					

Passage/ Lesson	Lesson/Passage Name	Q No.	Page No.	Practice		Mastered	Re-practice /Reteach
				Date	Score		
Lesson 3	Functions Of Language		77				
		1					
		2					
		3					
		4					
		5					
		6					
		7					
		8					
		9					
		10					
Lesson 4	Determining Unknown Words		81				
		1					
		2					
		3					
		4					
		5					
		6					
		7					
		8					
		9					
		10					

Passage/ Lesson	Lesson/Passage Name	Q No.	Page No.	Practice		Mastered	Re-practice /Reteach
				Date	Score		
Lesson 5	Figurative Language		85				
		1					
		2					
		3					
		4					
		5					
		6					
		7					
		8					
		9					
		10					
Lesson 6	Academic and Domain -Specific Vocabulary		89				
		1					
		2					
		3					
		4					
		5					
		6					
		7					
		8					
		9					
		10					

Passage/ Lesson	Lesson/Passage Name	Q No.	Page No.	Practice		Mastered	Re-practice /Reteach
				Date	Score		
Chapter 5	Writing		93				
Lesson 1	Writing Arguments To Support Claims		93				
		1					
		2					
		3					
		4					
		5					
		6					
		7					
		8					
		9					
		10					
Lesson 2	Writing Informative /Explanatory Texts		96				
		1					
		2					
		3					
		4					
		5					
Lesson 3	Write Narratives		99				
		1					
		2					
		3					
		4					
		5					
		6					
		7					
		8					
		9					
		10					

Passage/ Lesson	Lesson/Passage Name	Q No.	Page No.	Practice		Mastered	Re-practice /Reteach
				Date	Score		
Lesson 4	Produce Clear and Coherent Writing		102				
		1					
		2					
		3					
		4					
		5					
		6					
		7					
		8					
		9					
		10					
Lesson 5	Develop and Strengthening Writing		106				
		1					
		2					
		3					
		4					
		5					
		6					
		7					
		8					
		9					
		10					

Passage/ Lesson	Lesson/Passage Name	Q No.	Page No.	Practice		Mastered	Re-practice /Reteach
				Date	Score		
Lesson 6	Using Technologu to Produce ,Publish,and Update Writing Products		109				
		1					
		2					
		3					
		4					
		5					
		6					
		7					
		8					
		9					
		10					
Lesson 7	Conduct Short and Sustained Research Project		112				
		1					
		2					
		3					
		4					
		5					
Lesson 8	Source -Based Writing		115				
		1					
		2					
		3					
		4					
		5					
		6					
		7					
		8					
		9					
		10					

Passage/ Lesson	Lesson/Passage Name	Q No.	Page No.	Practice		Mastered	Re-practice /Reteach
				Date	Score		
Lesson 9	Citing Text-Evidence		120				
		1					
		2					
		3					
		4					
		5					
		6					
		7					
		8					
		9					
		10					

Passage/ Lesson	Lesson/Passage Name	Q No.	Page No.	Practice		Mastered	Re-practice /Reteach
				Date	Score		
	Additional Practice Questions		127				
		1					
		2					
		3					
		4					
		5					
		6					
		7					
		8					
		9					
		10					
		11					
		12					
		13					
		14					
		15					
		16					
		17					
		18					
		19					
		20					
		21					
		22					

Made in the USA
Middletown, DE
12 June 2024